HOW TO DRAW "ALMOST" EVERYTHING FOR KIDS

300 CUTE STEP-BY-STEP DRAWINGS OF ANIMALS, FOOD, CARS, FANTASY AND OTHER AMAZING STUFF!

This belongs to :

....

Special Art Learning

"How to Draw 'Almost' Everything for Kids"

*300 Cute Step-by-Step Drawings of Animals, Food,
Cars, Fantasy and Other Amazing Stuff!*

© 2024 by Special Art

Published by Special Art Books
www.specialartbooks.com

Paperback ISBN: 9791255532347
Images © Shutterstock

Table of Contents

Animals

Food and Treats

ACORN 24

APPLE 24

APRICOT 24

AVOCADO 25

BACON AND EGG 25

BANANA 25

BEET 26

BITTEN WATERMELON 26

BLUEBERRIES 26

BROCCOLI 27

BUBBLE TEA 27

BURGER 27

CANDY 28

CARROT 28

CHERRY 28

CHICKEN DRUMSTICK 29

COCONUT 29

COFFEE 29

CROISSANT 30

CUPCAKE 30

DOUGHNUT 30

EGGPLANT 31

FRUITCAKE 31

GINGERBREAD 31

GRAPES 32

GREEN PEAS 32

HOT DOG 32

JAMROLL 33

KETCHUP 33

LETTUCE 33

LOLLIPOP 34

LYCHEE 34

MANDARIN 34

MANGO 35

MANGOSTEEN 35

MUSHROOM 35

NOODLES 36

ONION 36

PAPAYA 36

PATTYPAN SQUASH 37

PEAR 37

PEPPER 37

PERSIMMON 38

PIECE OF CAKE 38

PINEAPPLE 38

PIZZA 39

POMEGRANATE 39

POPSICLE 39

PUDDING 40

PUMPKIN 40

RADISH 40

RASPBERRY 41

SAUSAGE 41

SLICED BREAD 41

STEAK 42

SUNDAE 42

TEMPURA 42

TOMATO 43

WATERMELON 43

ZUCCHINI 43

Vehicles and Transportation

Fantasy and Adventure

Everyday Objects

INTRODUCTION

Have you ever wanted to draw something but didn't know how to start? You have an idea of what you want to draw, but when you pick up your pencil, you think that it's too difficult. Let me tell you a secret: drawing amazing things doesn't have to be difficult!

Artists start from basic shapes, and when connected a certain way, these shapes begin to form amazing things like fantasy scenes, cool vehicles, and even cute animals! With this book, you'll learn how to use your imagination and your creativity to express yourself with drawings. You are an artist, and soon, you can display your works of art or give them out to your family and friends. With one stroke at a time, you'll learn how to draw "almost" everything!

How to Use This Book

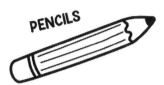

You don't need a lot of tools when you practice drawing. You can use your favorite pencil and some of the crayons that you already have. Mistakes can happen, so remember to keep an eraser close by too! If you want to add some color to your artwork, consider these additional supplies:

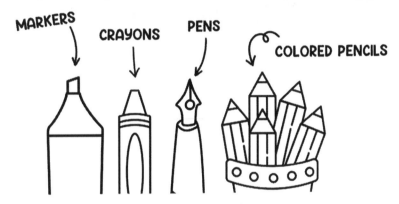

When sketching with your pencil, draw gently to keep your lines clean and make corrections easy. Lightly trace and follow the arrows to complete your drawing. Afterwards, there's space for you to practice drawing on each activity page. Use the pages of this book as your drawing space and fill it up with your art—yes, you can even draw on the margins!

So what are you waiting for? Start drawing and have fun!

Animals

What's your favorite **animal**? Is it a colorful **butterfly**?
Or the mysterious **narwhal**? Or the fluffy **rabbit**?
In this chapter, you'll learn to **draw** some of the cutest and
most interesting **animals**.

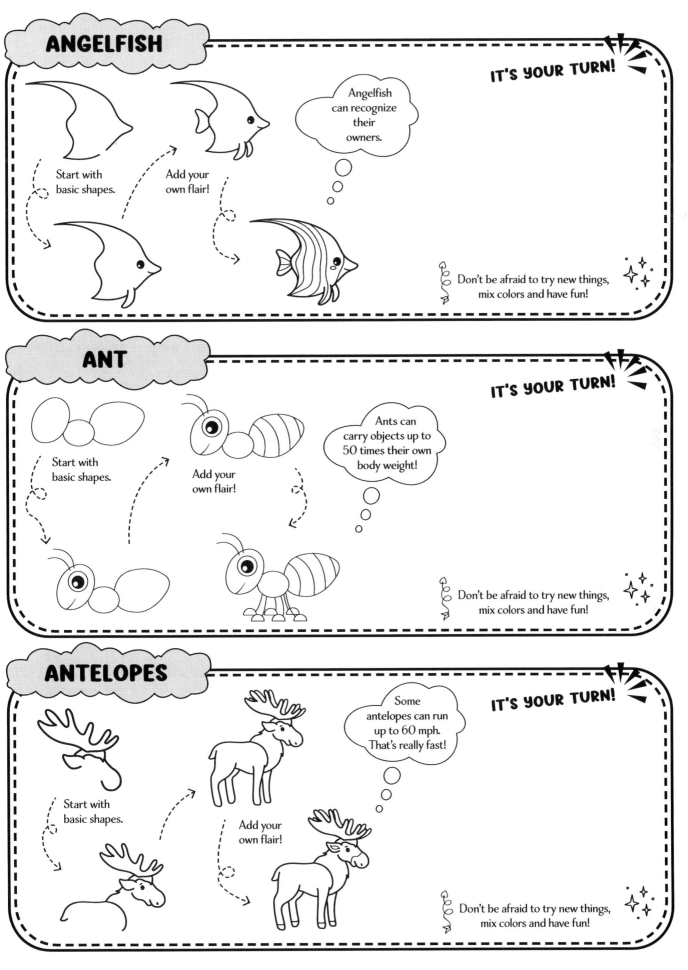

AXOLOTL

Start with basic shapes.

Add your own flair!

Axolotls can regrow entire limbs and even parts of their heart and brain.

IT'S YOUR TURN!

Don't be afraid to try new things, mix colors and have fun!

BAT

Start with basic shapes.

Add your own flair!

Bats are the only mammals that can fly for a long time.

IT'S YOUR TURN!

Don't be afraid to try new things, mix colors and have fun!

BEAR

Start with basic shapes.

Add your own flair!

Bears have a powerful sense of smell, even better than dogs.

IT'S YOUR TURN!

Don't be afraid to try new things, mix colors and have fun!

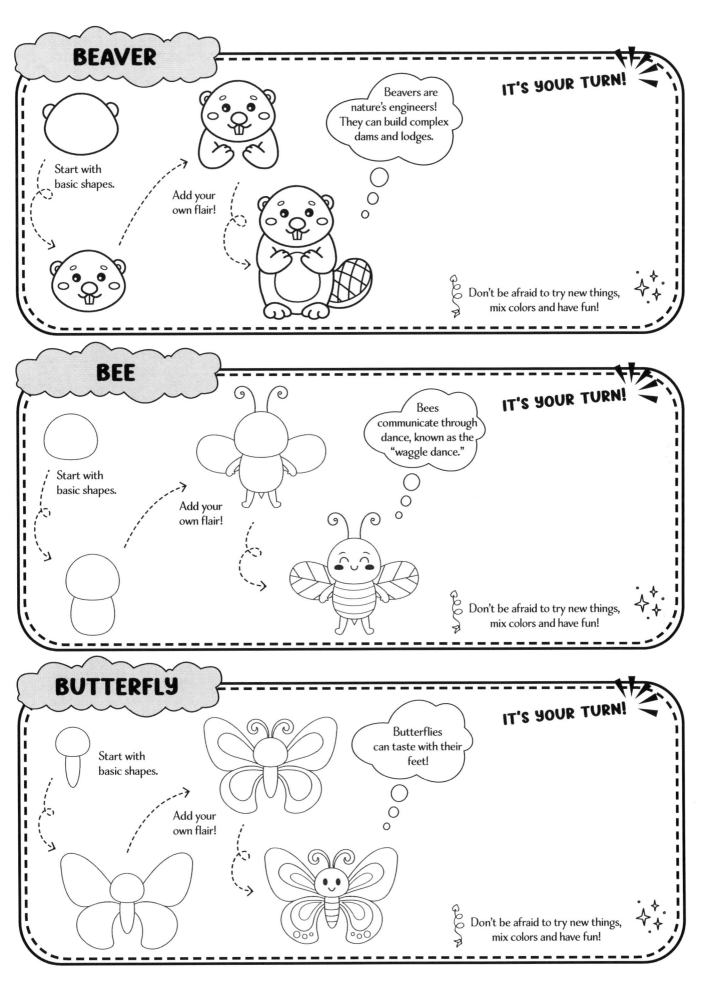

 5

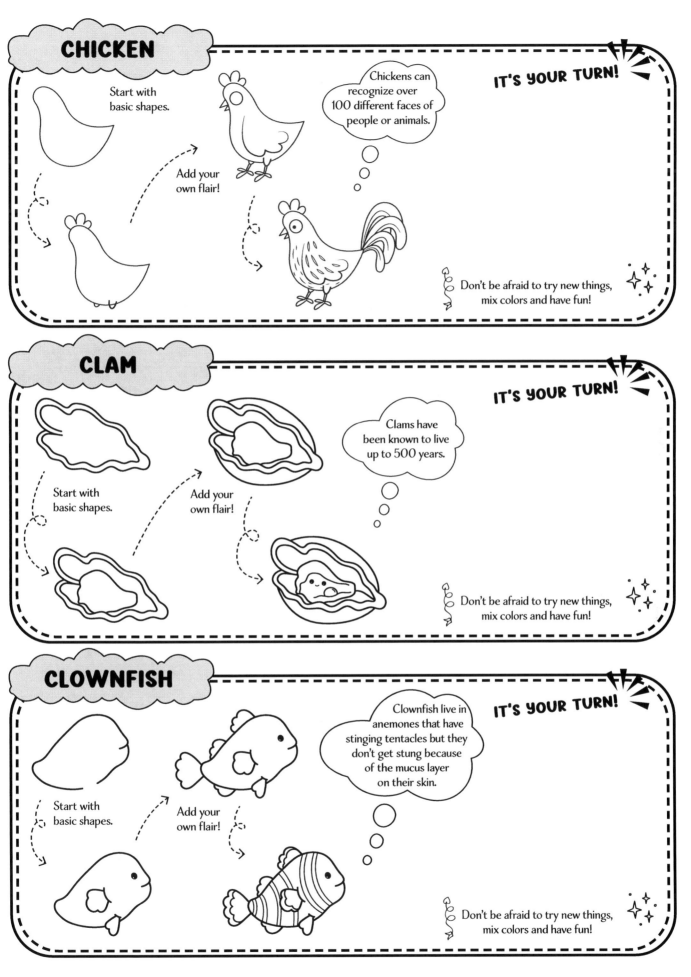

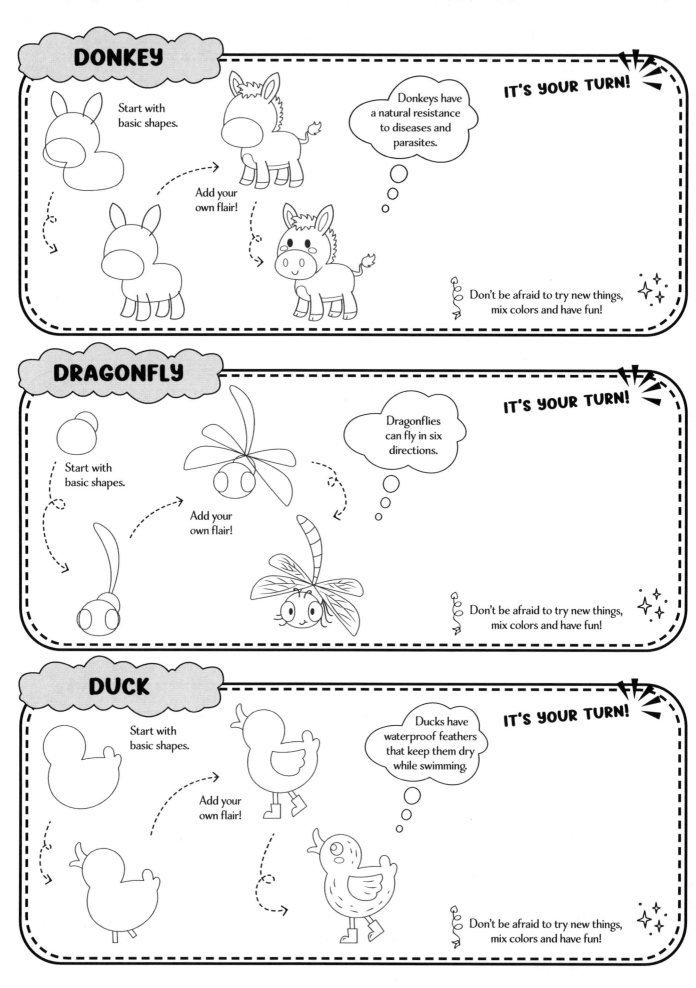

FLY

Start with basic shapes.

Add your own flair!

Flies have a short lifespan, typically living for only about 30 days.

IT'S YOUR TURN!

Don't be afraid to try new things, mix colors and have fun!

FOX

Start with basic shapes.

Add your own flair!

Foxes use the Earth's magnetic field to hunt.

IT'S YOUR TURN!

Don't be afraid to try new things, mix colors and have fun!

GIRAFFE

Start with basic shapes.

Add your own flair!

Our necks can grow to around six feet long!

IT'S YOUR TURN!

Don't be afraid to try new things, mix colors and have fun!

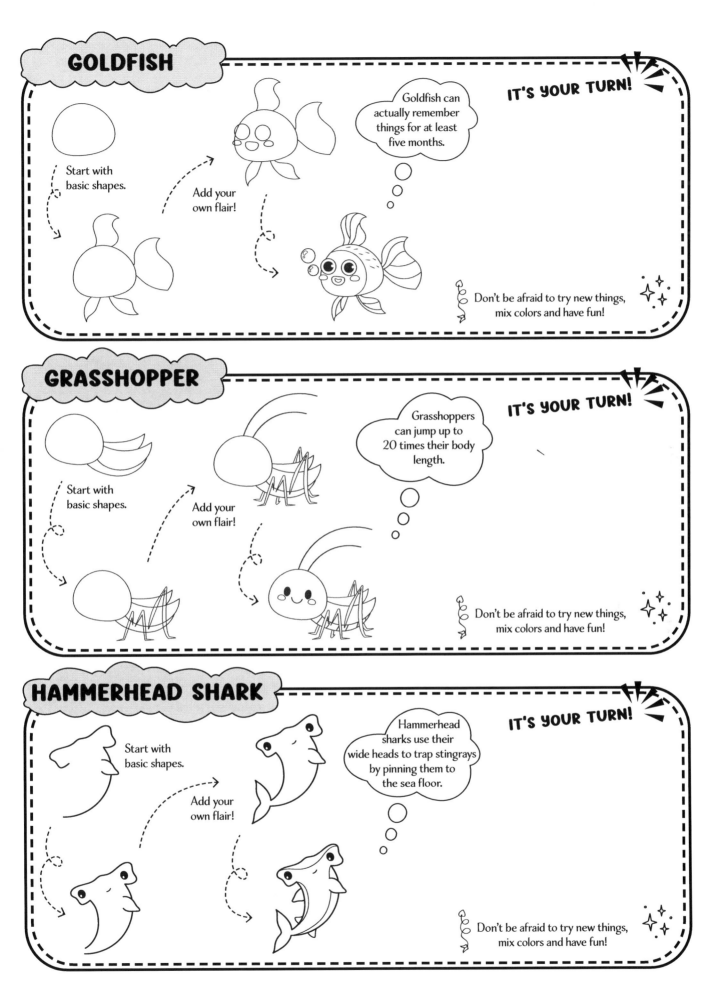

GOLDFISH

Start with basic shapes.

Add your own flair!

Goldfish can actually remember things for at least five months.

IT'S YOUR TURN!

Don't be afraid to try new things, mix colors and have fun!

GRASSHOPPER

Start with basic shapes.

Add your own flair!

Grasshoppers can jump up to 20 times their body length.

IT'S YOUR TURN!

Don't be afraid to try new things, mix colors and have fun!

HAMMERHEAD SHARK

Start with basic shapes.

Add your own flair!

Hammerhead sharks use their wide heads to trap stingrays by pinning them to the sea floor.

IT'S YOUR TURN!

Don't be afraid to try new things, mix colors and have fun!

13

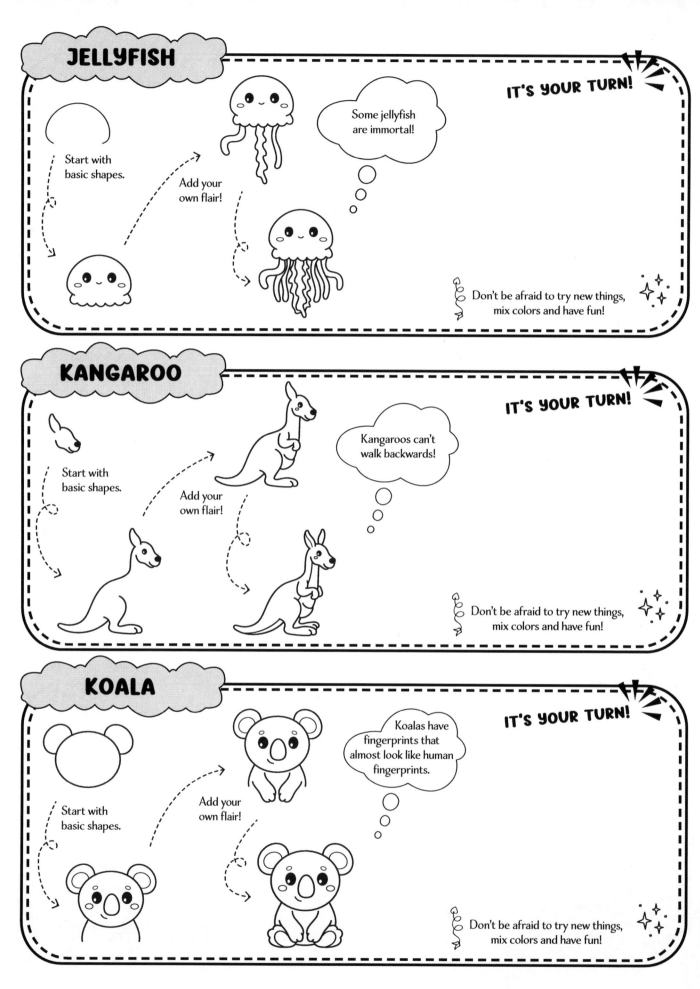

OCTOPUS

Start with basic shapes.

Add your own flair!

Octopuses have three hearts and blue blood.

IT'S YOUR TURN!

Don't be afraid to try new things, mix colors and have fun!

OYSTER

Start with basic shapes.

Add your own flair!

Some oysters can produce pearls, which are formed because they get irritated by dust particles.

IT'S YOUR TURN!

Don't be afraid to try new things, mix colors and have fun!

PUFFERFISH

Start with basic shapes.

Add your own flair!

Pufferfish can inflate their bodies to avoid predators.

IT'S YOUR TURN!

Don't be afraid to try new things, mix colors and have fun!

18

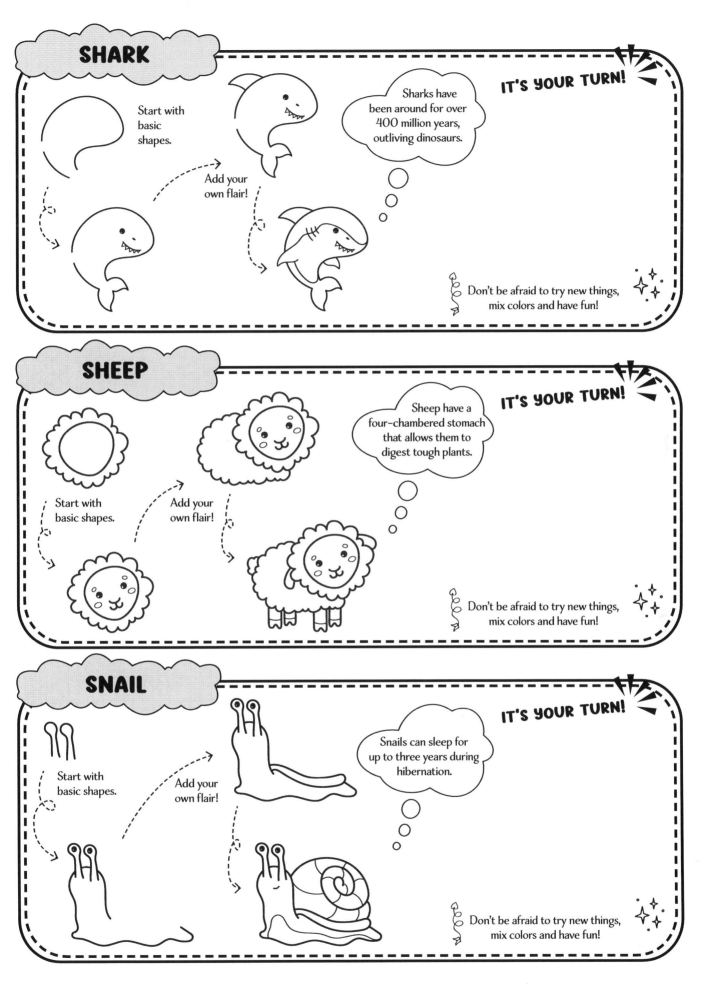

19

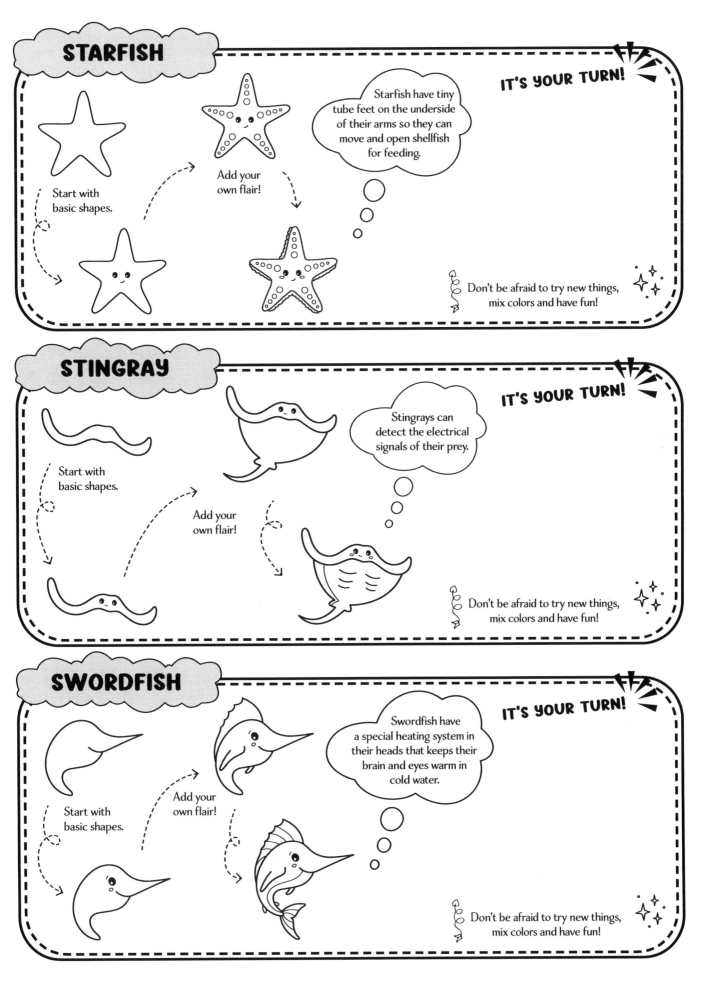

Food and Treats

We all need to **eat!**

In this chapter, you'll learn how to draw a buffet of delicious and healthy **fruits, vegetables,** and even **desserts!**

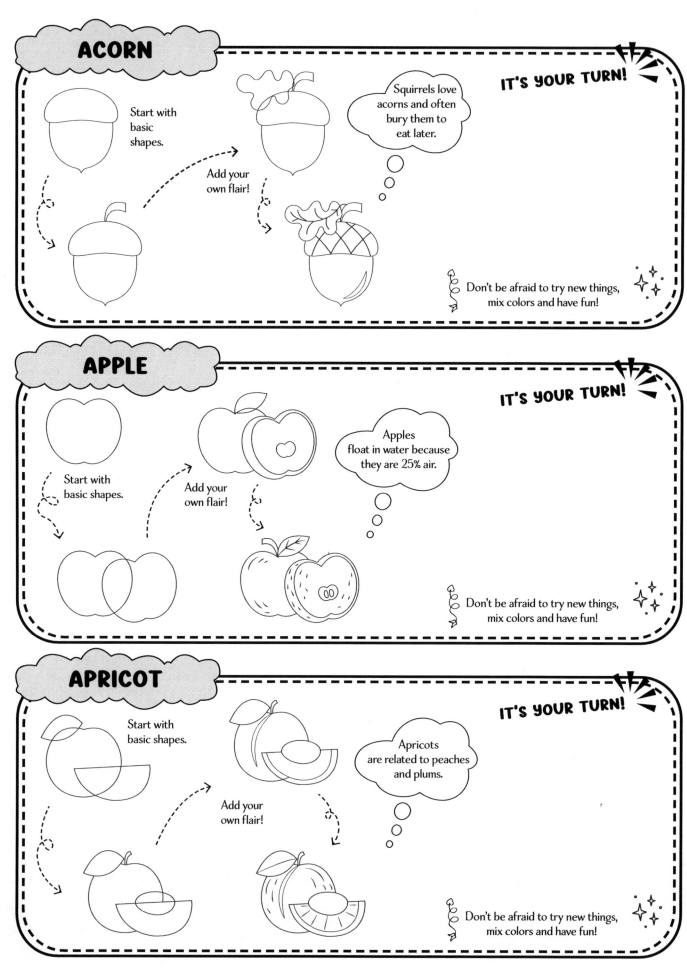

ACORN

Start with basic shapes.

Add your own flair!

Squirrels love acorns and often bury them to eat later.

IT'S YOUR TURN!

Don't be afraid to try new things, mix colors and have fun!

APPLE

Start with basic shapes.

Add your own flair!

Apples float in water because they are 25% air.

IT'S YOUR TURN!

Don't be afraid to try new things, mix colors and have fun!

APRICOT

Start with basic shapes.

Add your own flair!

Apricots are related to peaches and plums.

IT'S YOUR TURN!

Don't be afraid to try new things, mix colors and have fun!

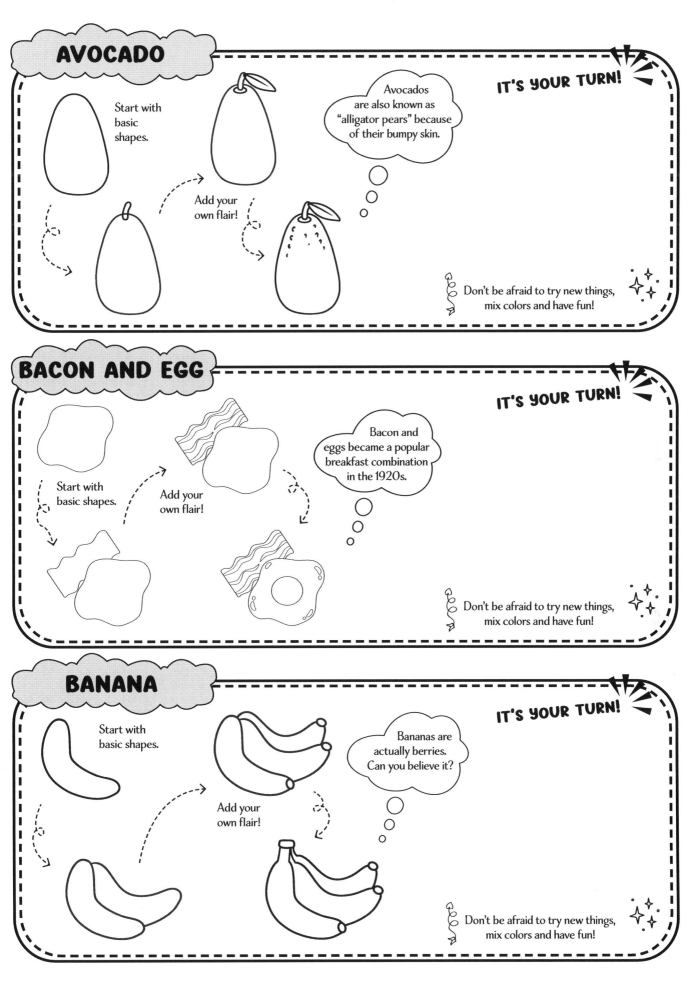

AVOCADO

Start with basic shapes.

Add your own flair!

Avocados are also known as "alligator pears" because of their bumpy skin.

IT'S YOUR TURN!

Don't be afraid to try new things, mix colors and have fun!

BACON AND EGG

Start with basic shapes.

Add your own flair!

Bacon and eggs became a popular breakfast combination in the 1920s.

IT'S YOUR TURN!

Don't be afraid to try new things, mix colors and have fun!

BANANA

Start with basic shapes.

Add your own flair!

Bananas are actually berries. Can you believe it?

IT'S YOUR TURN!

Don't be afraid to try new things, mix colors and have fun!

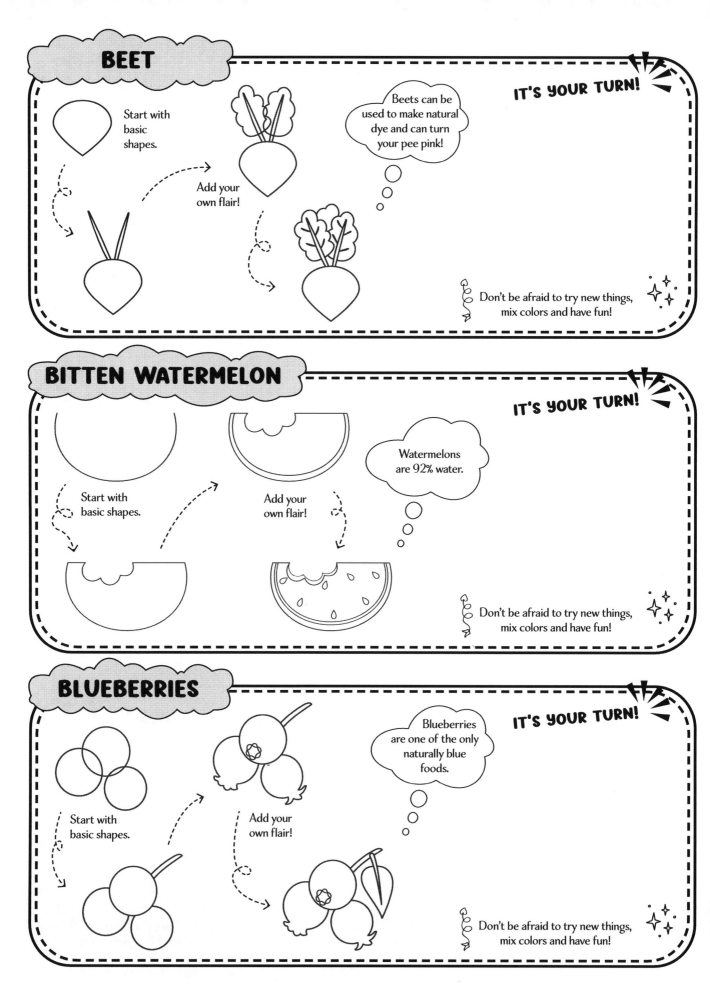

BEET

Start with basic shapes.

Add your own flair!

Beets can be used to make natural dye and can turn your pee pink!

IT'S YOUR TURN!

Don't be afraid to try new things, mix colors and have fun!

BITTEN WATERMELON

Start with basic shapes.

Add your own flair!

Watermelons are 92% water.

IT'S YOUR TURN!

Don't be afraid to try new things, mix colors and have fun!

BLUEBERRIES

Start with basic shapes.

Add your own flair!

Blueberries are one of the only naturally blue foods.

IT'S YOUR TURN!

Don't be afraid to try new things, mix colors and have fun!

BROCCOLI

Start with basic shapes.

Add your own flair!

Broccoli has more vitamin C than an orange.

IT'S YOUR TURN!

Don't be afraid to try new things, mix colors and have fun!

BUBBLE TEA

Start with basic shapes.

Add your own flair!

Bubble tea, also known as boba tea, has chewy tapioca pearls at the bottom of the drink.

IT'S YOUR TURN!

Don't be afraid to try new things, mix colors and have fun!

BURGER

Start with basic shapes.

Add your own flair!

The largest burger ever made weighed over 2,000 pounds!

IT'S YOUR TURN!

Don't be afraid to try new things, mix colors and have fun!

 27

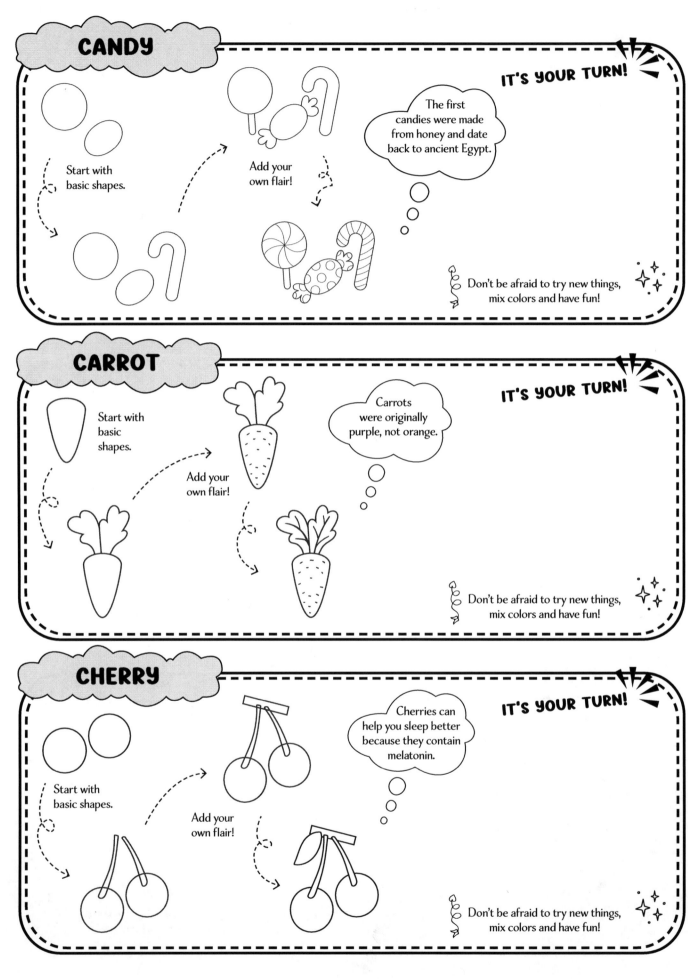

CANDY

Start with basic shapes.

Add your own flair!

The first candies were made from honey and date back to ancient Egypt.

IT'S YOUR TURN!

Don't be afraid to try new things, mix colors and have fun!

CARROT

Start with basic shapes.

Add your own flair!

Carrots were originally purple, not orange.

IT'S YOUR TURN!

Don't be afraid to try new things, mix colors and have fun!

CHERRY

Start with basic shapes.

Add your own flair!

Cherries can help you sleep better because they contain melatonin.

IT'S YOUR TURN!

Don't be afraid to try new things, mix colors and have fun!

CHICKEN DRUMSTICK

IT'S YOUR TURN!

Start with basic shapes.

Add your own flair!

Chicken drumsticks are named after the drumsticks used by musicians.

Don't be afraid to try new things, mix colors and have fun!

COCONUT

IT'S YOUR TURN!

Start with basic shapes.

Add your own flair!

Coconuts can float on water and travel across oceans to sprout on new beaches.

Don't be afraid to try new things, mix colors and have fun!

COFFEE

IT'S YOUR TURN!

Start with basic shapes.

Add your own flair!

Coffee beans are actually seeds from the berries of the coffee plant.

Don't be afraid to try new things, mix colors and have fun!

CROISSANT

Start with basic shapes.

Add your own flair!

IT'S YOUR TURN!

Croissants were first made in Austria, not France.

Don't be afraid to try new things, mix colors and have fun!

CUPCAKE

Start with basic shapes.

Add your own flair!

IT'S YOUR TURN!

Cupcakes got their name because they were originally baked in small cups.

Don't be afraid to try new things, mix colors and have fun!

DOUGHNUT

IT'S YOUR TURN!

Doughnuts were first made with holes to cook more evenly.

Start with basic shapes.

Add your own flair!

Don't be afraid to try new things, mix colors and have fun!

GRAPES

Start with basic shapes.

Add your own flair!

Grapes can catch fire and even explode in the microwave! Don't try it at home!

IT'S YOUR TURN!

Don't be afraid to try new things, mix colors and have fun!

GREEN PEAS

Start with basic shapes.

Add your own flair!

Green peas are one of the oldest cultivated crops and have been eaten for thousands of years.

IT'S YOUR TURN!

Don't be afraid to try new things, mix colors and have fun!

HOT DOG

Start with basic shapes.

Add your own flair!

Hot dogs were first sold in buns at the 1904 World's Fair in St. Louis.

IT'S YOUR TURN!

Don't be afraid to try new things, mix colors and have fun!

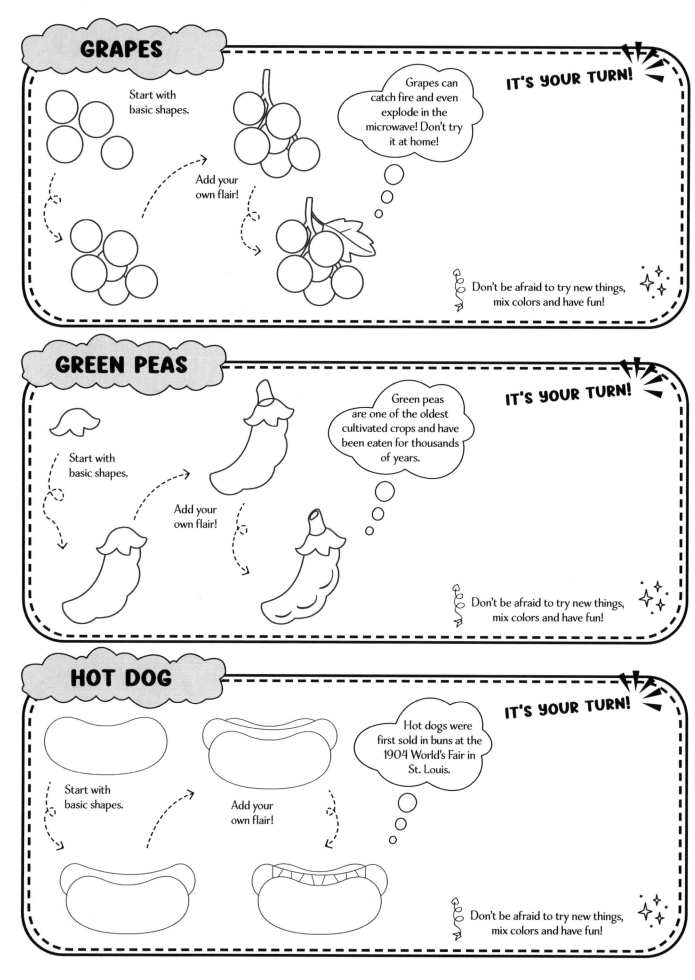

32

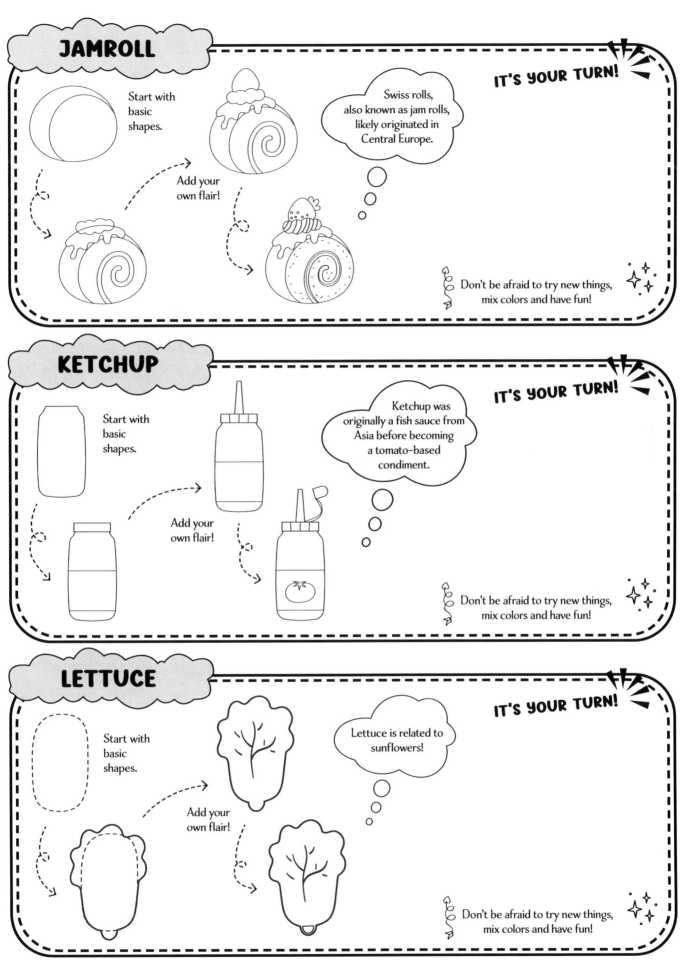

JAMROLL

Start with basic shapes.

Add your own flair!

Swiss rolls, also known as jam rolls, likely originated in Central Europe.

IT'S YOUR TURN!

Don't be afraid to try new things, mix colors and have fun!

KETCHUP

Start with basic shapes.

Add your own flair!

Ketchup was originally a fish sauce from Asia before becoming a tomato-based condiment.

IT'S YOUR TURN!

Don't be afraid to try new things, mix colors and have fun!

LETTUCE

Start with basic shapes.

Add your own flair!

Lettuce is related to sunflowers!

IT'S YOUR TURN!

Don't be afraid to try new things, mix colors and have fun!

33

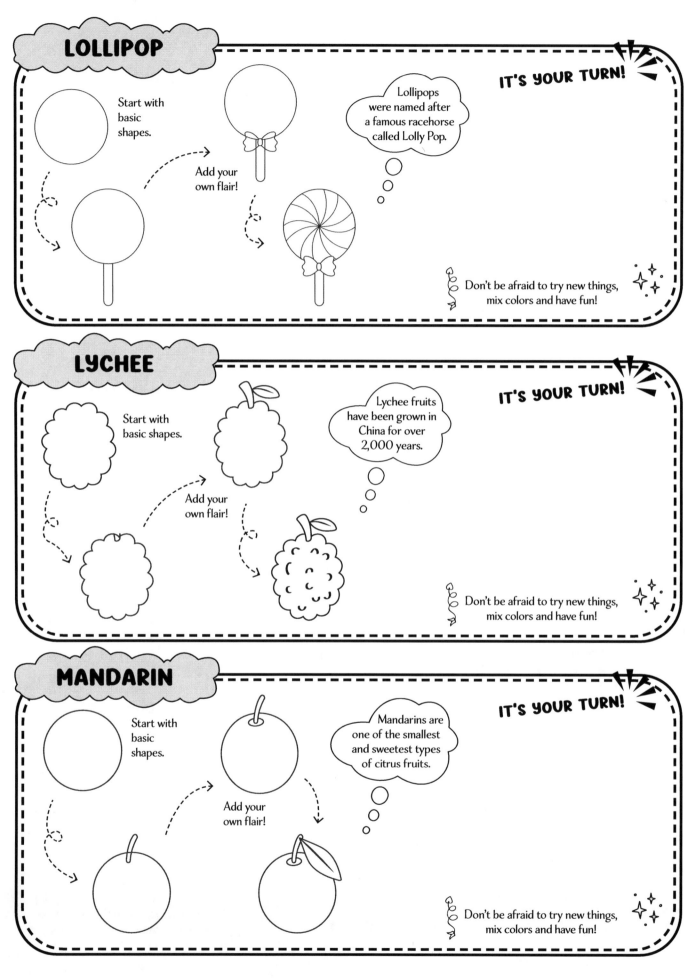

LOLLIPOP

Start with basic shapes.

Add your own flair!

IT'S YOUR TURN!

Lollipops were named after a famous racehorse called Lolly Pop.

Don't be afraid to try new things, mix colors and have fun!

LYCHEE

Start with basic shapes.

Add your own flair!

IT'S YOUR TURN!

Lychee fruits have been grown in China for over 2,000 years.

Don't be afraid to try new things, mix colors and have fun!

MANDARIN

Start with basic shapes.

Add your own flair!

IT'S YOUR TURN!

Mandarins are one of the smallest and sweetest types of citrus fruits.

Don't be afraid to try new things, mix colors and have fun!

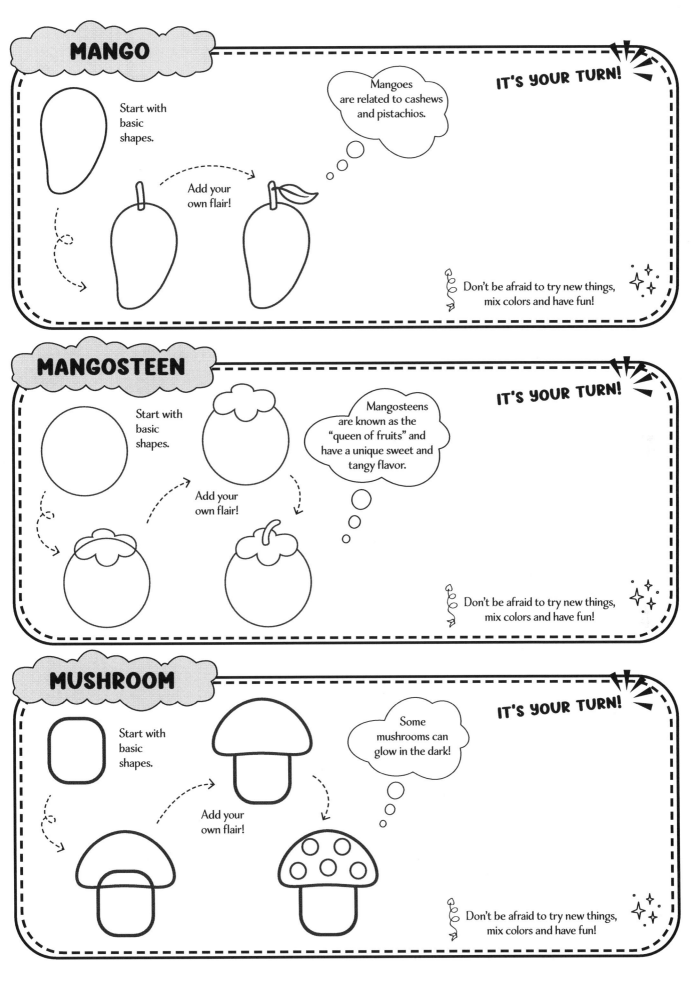

MANGO

Start with basic shapes.

Add your own flair!

Mangoes are related to cashews and pistachios.

IT'S YOUR TURN!

Don't be afraid to try new things, mix colors and have fun!

MANGOSTEEN

Start with basic shapes.

Add your own flair!

Mangosteens are known as the "queen of fruits" and have a unique sweet and tangy flavor.

IT'S YOUR TURN!

Don't be afraid to try new things, mix colors and have fun!

MUSHROOM

Start with basic shapes.

Add your own flair!

Some mushrooms can glow in the dark!

IT'S YOUR TURN!

Don't be afraid to try new things, mix colors and have fun!

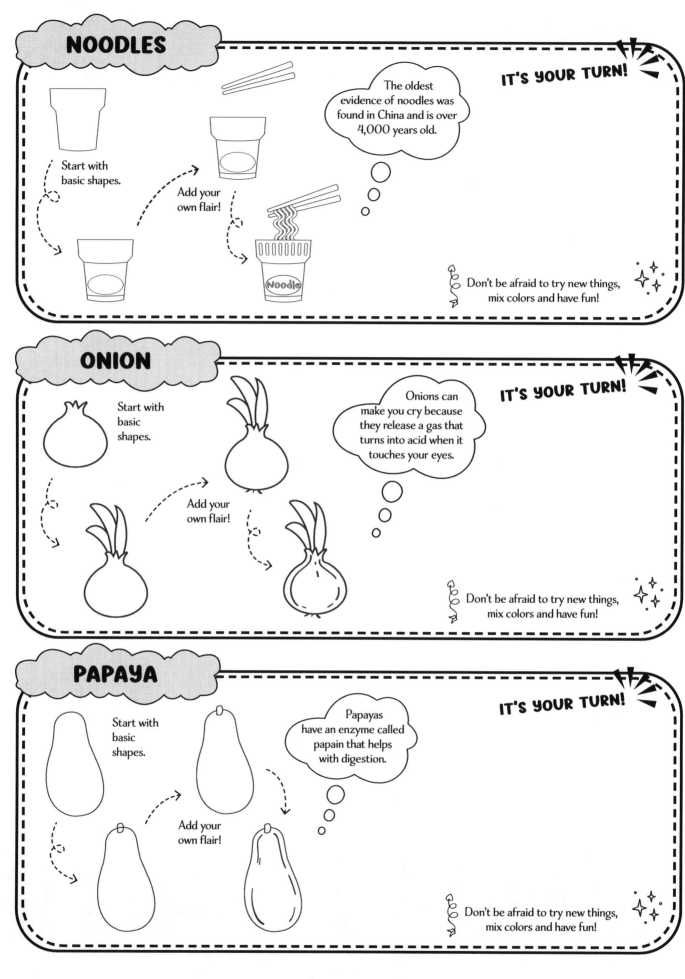

NOODLES

Start with basic shapes.

Add your own flair!

The oldest evidence of noodles was found in China and is over 4,000 years old.

IT'S YOUR TURN!

Noodle

Don't be afraid to try new things, mix colors and have fun!

ONION

Start with basic shapes.

Add your own flair!

Onions can make you cry because they release a gas that turns into acid when it touches your eyes.

IT'S YOUR TURN!

Don't be afraid to try new things, mix colors and have fun!

PAPAYA

Start with basic shapes.

Add your own flair!

Papayas have an enzyme called papain that helps with digestion.

IT'S YOUR TURN!

Don't be afraid to try new things, mix colors and have fun!

36

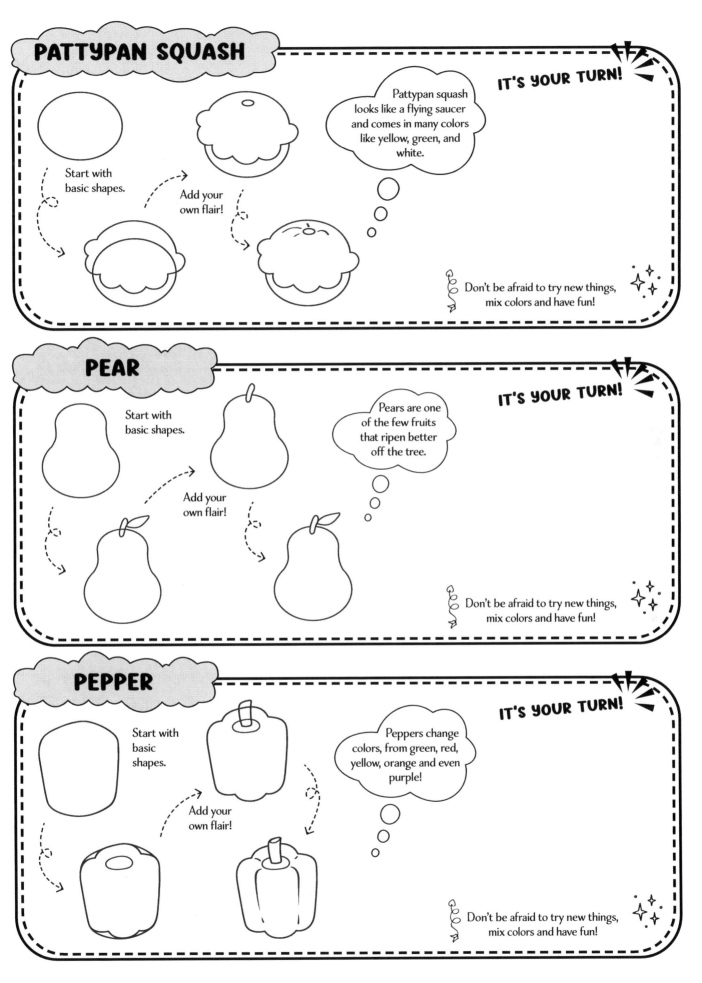

PATTYPAN SQUASH

IT'S YOUR TURN!

Start with basic shapes.

Add your own flair!

Pattypan squash looks like a flying saucer and comes in many colors like yellow, green, and white.

Don't be afraid to try new things, mix colors and have fun!

PEAR

IT'S YOUR TURN!

Start with basic shapes.

Add your own flair!

Pears are one of the few fruits that ripen better off the tree.

Don't be afraid to try new things, mix colors and have fun!

PEPPER

IT'S YOUR TURN!

Start with basic shapes.

Add your own flair!

Peppers change colors, from green, red, yellow, orange and even purple!

Don't be afraid to try new things, mix colors and have fun!

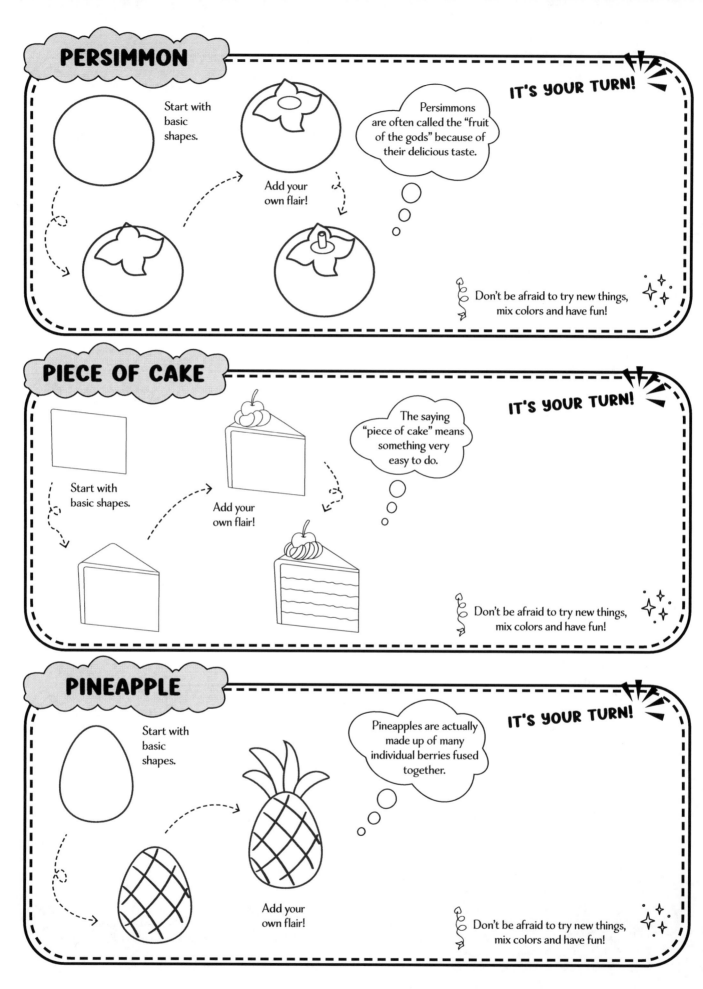

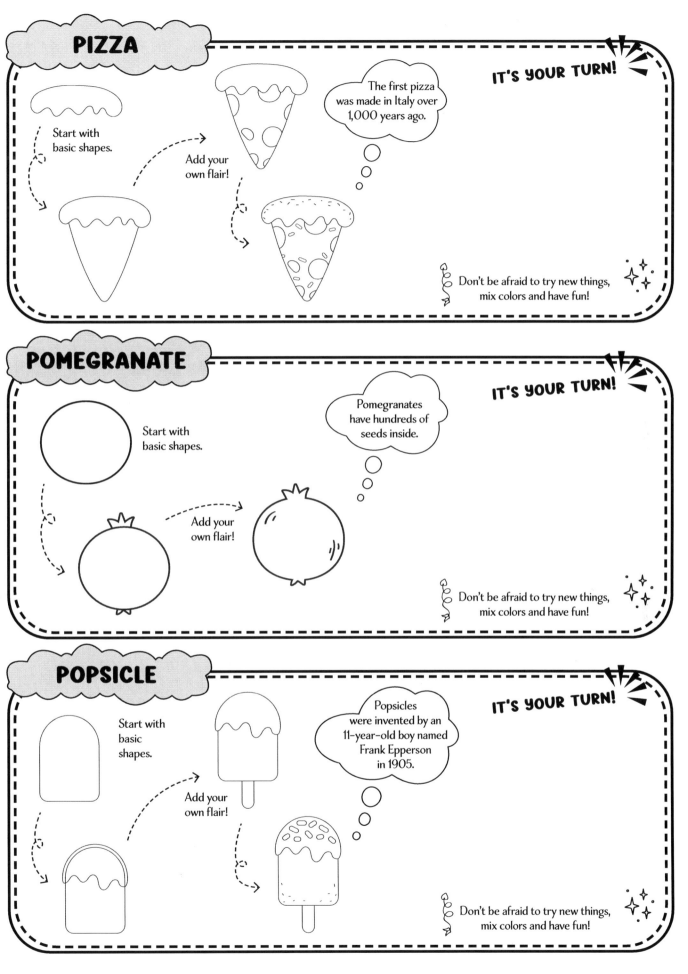

PIZZA

Start with basic shapes.

Add your own flair!

IT'S YOUR TURN!

The first pizza was made in Italy over 1,000 years ago.

Don't be afraid to try new things, mix colors and have fun!

POMEGRANATE

Start with basic shapes.

Add your own flair!

IT'S YOUR TURN!

Pomegranates have hundreds of seeds inside.

Don't be afraid to try new things, mix colors and have fun!

POPSICLE

Start with basic shapes.

Add your own flair!

IT'S YOUR TURN!

Popsicles were invented by an 11-year-old boy named Frank Epperson in 1905.

Don't be afraid to try new things, mix colors and have fun!

PUDDING

Start with basic shapes.

Add your own flair!

IT'S YOUR TURN!

Pudding can be both sweet and savory, depending on where you are in the world.

Don't be afraid to try new things, mix colors and have fun!

PUMPKIN

Start with basic shapes.

Add your own flair!

IT'S YOUR TURN!

Pumpkins are technically a fruit and can come in many colors like orange, white, and even blue!

Don't be afraid to try new things, mix colors and have fun!

RADISH

Start with basic shapes.

Add your own flair!

IT'S YOUR TURN!

Radishes were one of the first crops to be grown by humans and are often very crunchy.

Don't be afraid to try new things, mix colors and have fun!

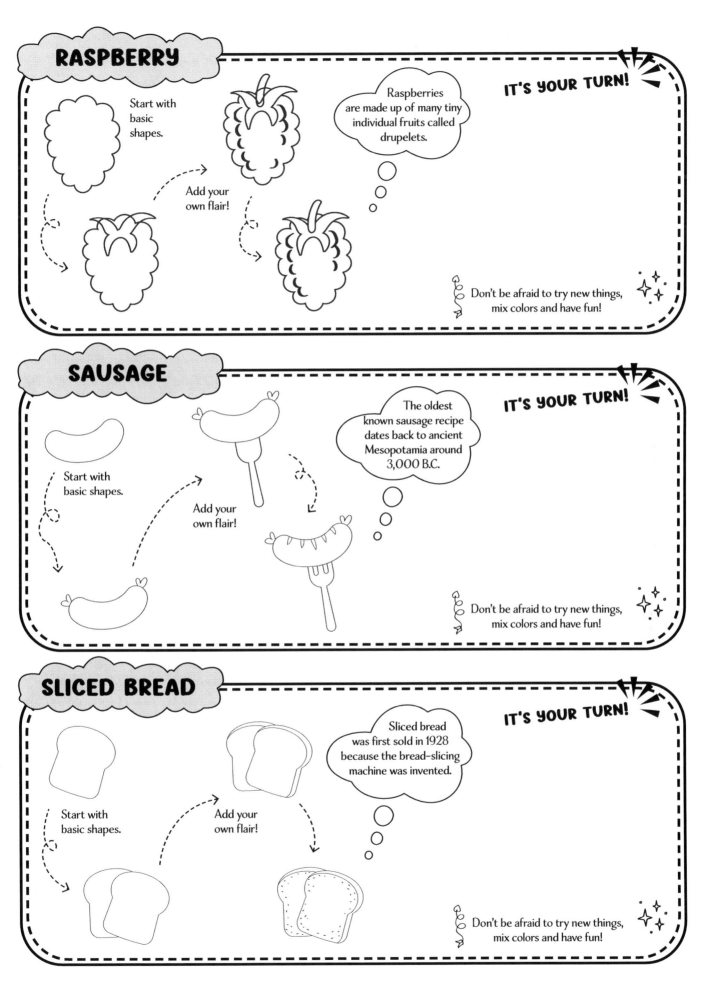

RASPBERRY

Start with basic shapes.

Add your own flair!

Raspberries are made up of many tiny individual fruits called drupelets.

IT'S YOUR TURN!

Don't be afraid to try new things, mix colors and have fun!

SAUSAGE

Start with basic shapes.

Add your own flair!

The oldest known sausage recipe dates back to ancient Mesopotamia around 3,000 B.C.

IT'S YOUR TURN!

Don't be afraid to try new things, mix colors and have fun!

SLICED BREAD

Start with basic shapes.

Add your own flair!

Sliced bread was first sold in 1928 because the bread-slicing machine was invented.

IT'S YOUR TURN!

Don't be afraid to try new things, mix colors and have fun!

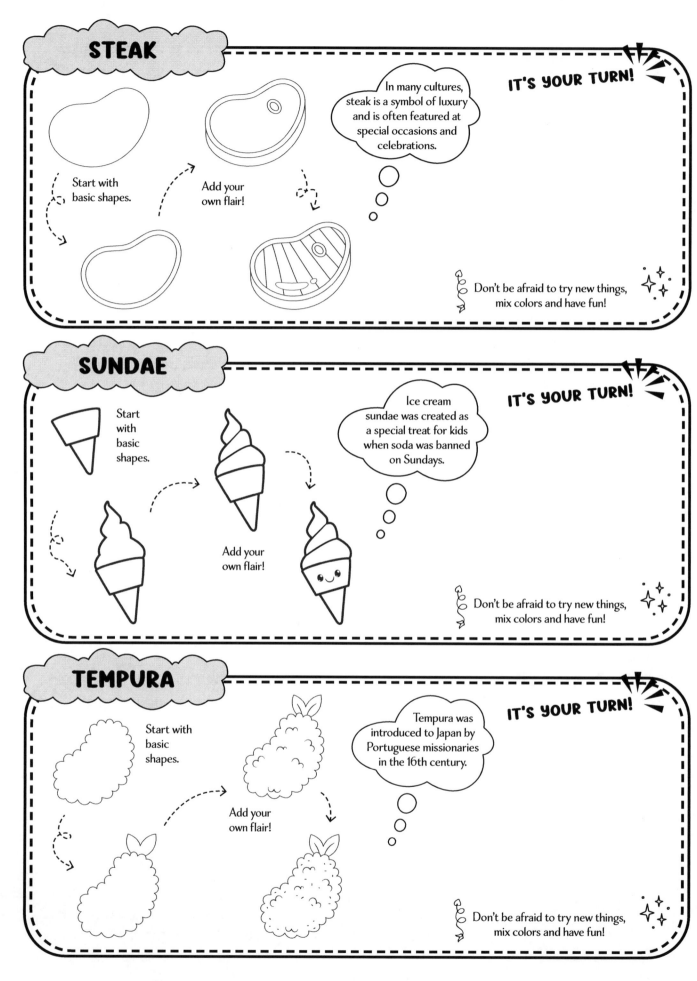

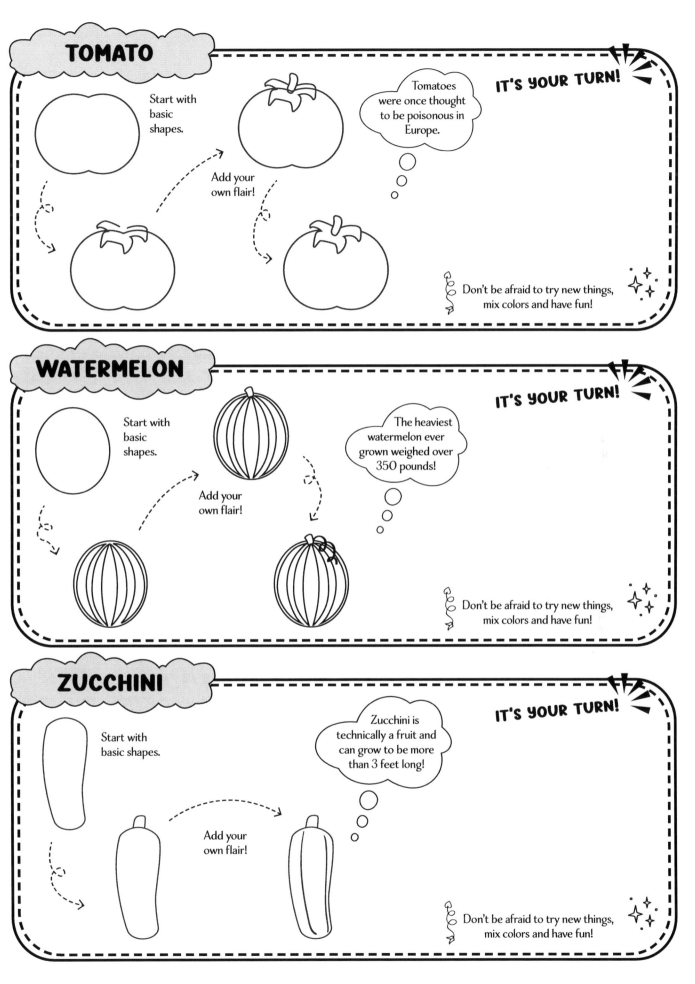

TOMATO

Start with basic shapes.

Add your own flair!

Tomatoes were once thought to be poisonous in Europe.

IT'S YOUR TURN!

Don't be afraid to try new things, mix colors and have fun!

WATERMELON

Start with basic shapes.

Add your own flair!

The heaviest watermelon ever grown weighed over 350 pounds!

IT'S YOUR TURN!

Don't be afraid to try new things, mix colors and have fun!

ZUCCHINI

Start with basic shapes.

Add your own flair!

Zucchini is technically a fruit and can grow to be more than 3 feet long!

IT'S YOUR TURN!

Don't be afraid to try new things, mix colors and have fun!

Vehicles and Transportation

Bring us to life with your colors!

Cars, planes, and boats—thanks to these amazing **vehicles**, you can go to so many places faster than just **walking!** In this chapter, get to know all the different kinds of **transportation** and learn how to draw your favorite **vehicle** to **travel** in!

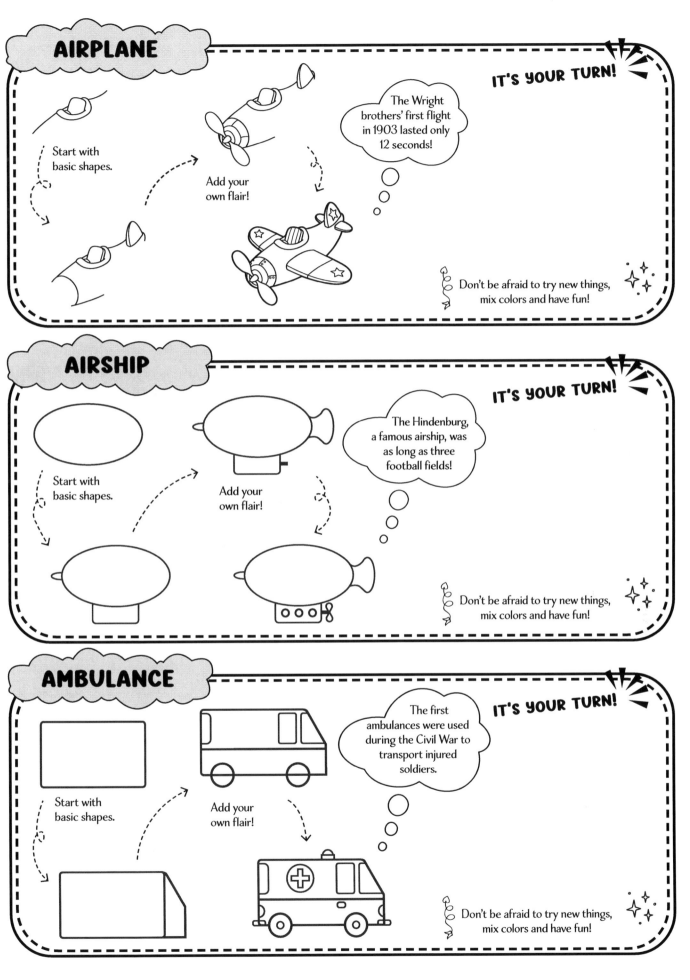

AIRPLANE

IT'S YOUR TURN!

Start with basic shapes.

Add your own flair!

The Wright brothers' first flight in 1903 lasted only 12 seconds!

Don't be afraid to try new things, mix colors and have fun!

AIRSHIP

IT'S YOUR TURN!

Start with basic shapes.

Add your own flair!

The Hindenburg, a famous airship, was as long as three football fields!

Don't be afraid to try new things, mix colors and have fun!

AMBULANCE

IT'S YOUR TURN!

Start with basic shapes.

Add your own flair!

The first ambulances were used during the Civil War to transport injured soldiers.

Don't be afraid to try new things, mix colors and have fun!

45

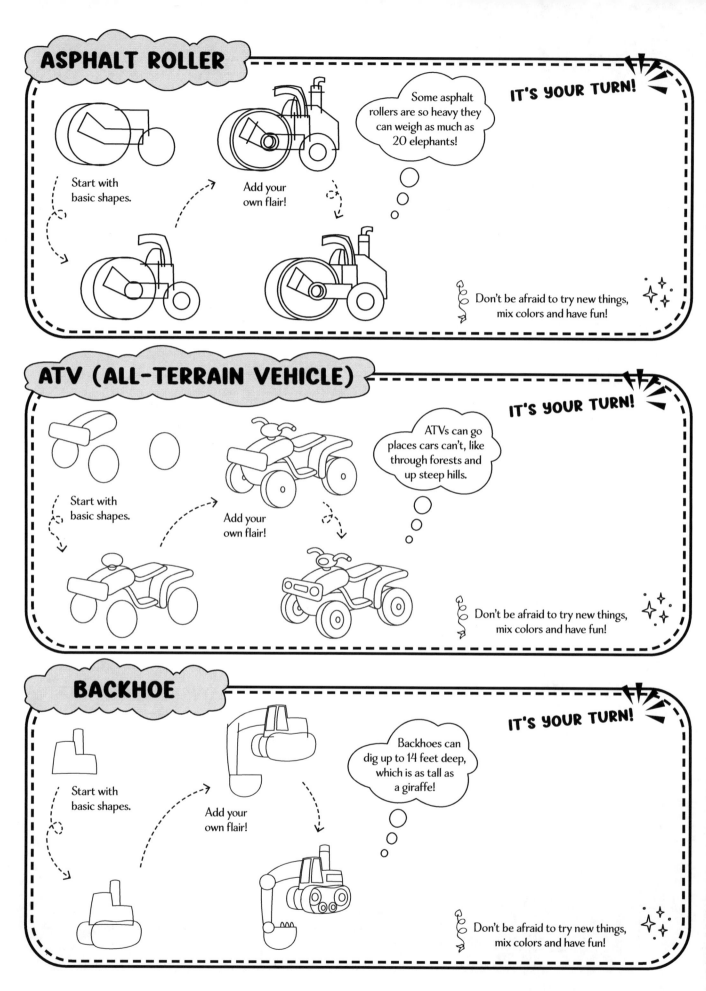

ASPHALT ROLLER

Start with basic shapes.

Add your own flair!

Some asphalt rollers are so heavy they can weigh as much as 20 elephants!

IT'S YOUR TURN!

Don't be afraid to try new things, mix colors and have fun!

ATV (ALL-TERRAIN VEHICLE)

Start with basic shapes.

Add your own flair!

ATVs can go places cars can't, like through forests and up steep hills.

IT'S YOUR TURN!

Don't be afraid to try new things, mix colors and have fun!

BACKHOE

Start with basic shapes.

Add your own flair!

Backhoes can dig up to 14 feet deep, which is as tall as a giraffe!

IT'S YOUR TURN!

Don't be afraid to try new things, mix colors and have fun!

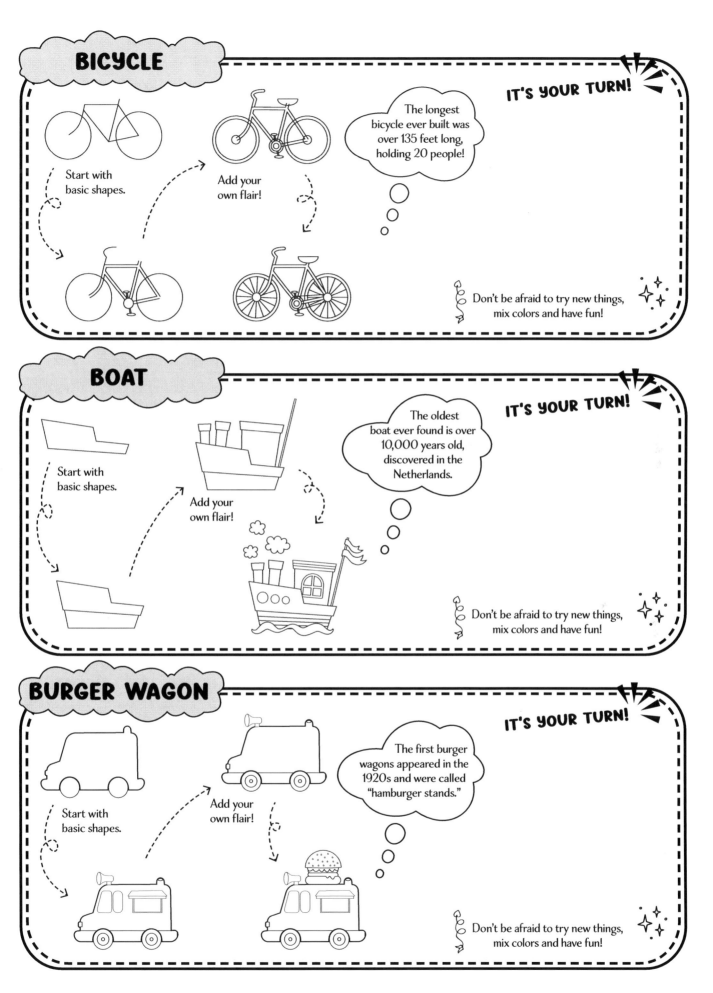

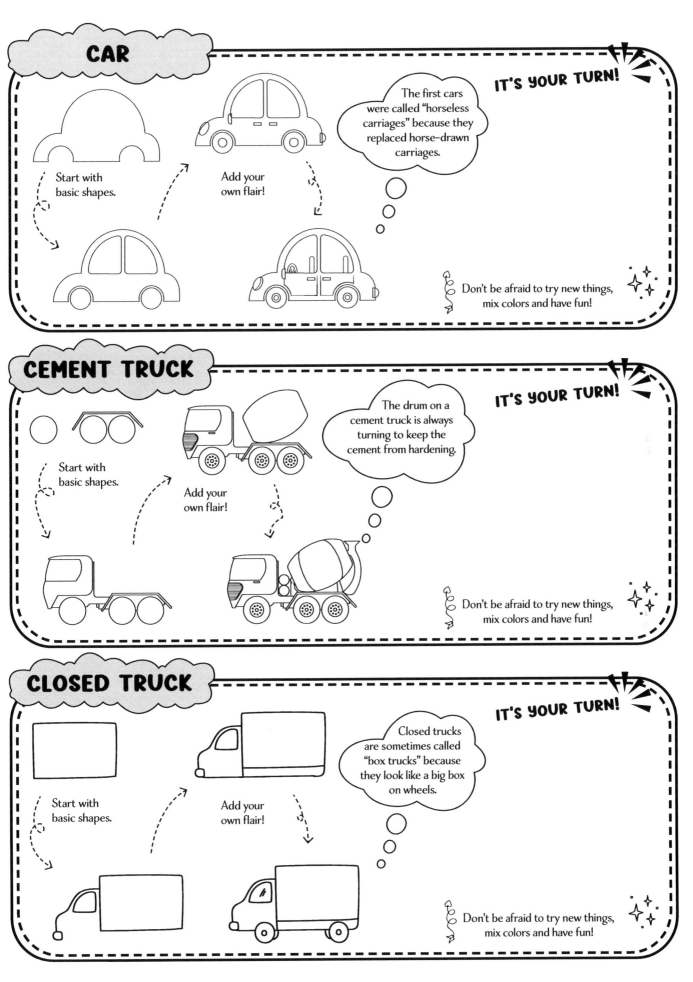

CAR

Start with basic shapes.

Add your own flair!

IT'S YOUR TURN!

The first cars were called "horseless carriages" because they replaced horse-drawn carriages.

Don't be afraid to try new things, mix colors and have fun!

CEMENT TRUCK

Start with basic shapes.

Add your own flair!

IT'S YOUR TURN!

The drum on a cement truck is always turning to keep the cement from hardening.

Don't be afraid to try new things, mix colors and have fun!

CLOSED TRUCK

Start with basic shapes.

Add your own flair!

IT'S YOUR TURN!

Closed trucks are sometimes called "box trucks" because they look like a big box on wheels.

Don't be afraid to try new things, mix colors and have fun!

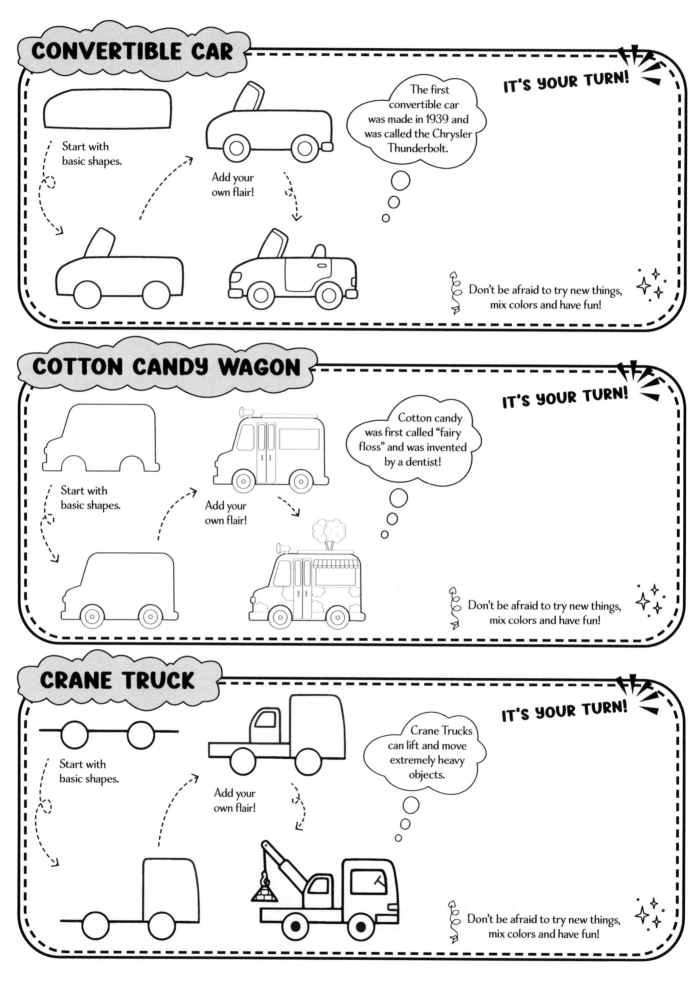

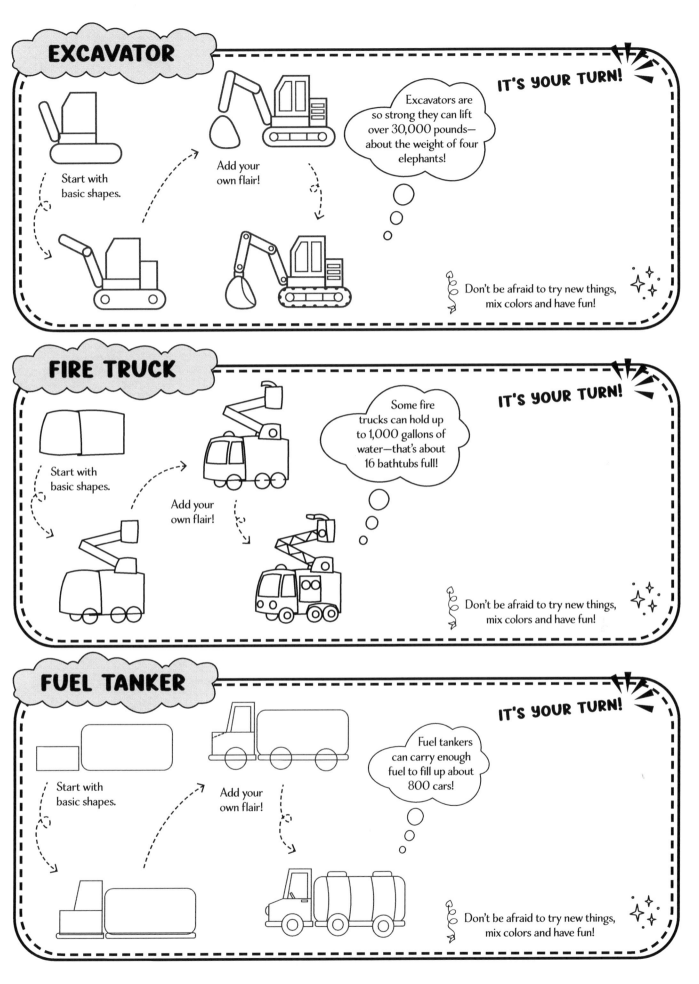

EXCAVATOR

IT'S YOUR TURN!

Start with basic shapes.

Add your own flair!

Excavators are so strong they can lift over 30,000 pounds— about the weight of four elephants!

Don't be afraid to try new things, mix colors and have fun!

FIRE TRUCK

IT'S YOUR TURN!

Start with basic shapes.

Add your own flair!

Some fire trucks can hold up to 1,000 gallons of water—that's about 16 bathtubs full!

Don't be afraid to try new things, mix colors and have fun!

FUEL TANKER

IT'S YOUR TURN!

Start with basic shapes.

Add your own flair!

Fuel tankers can carry enough fuel to fill up about 800 cars!

Don't be afraid to try new things, mix colors and have fun!

51

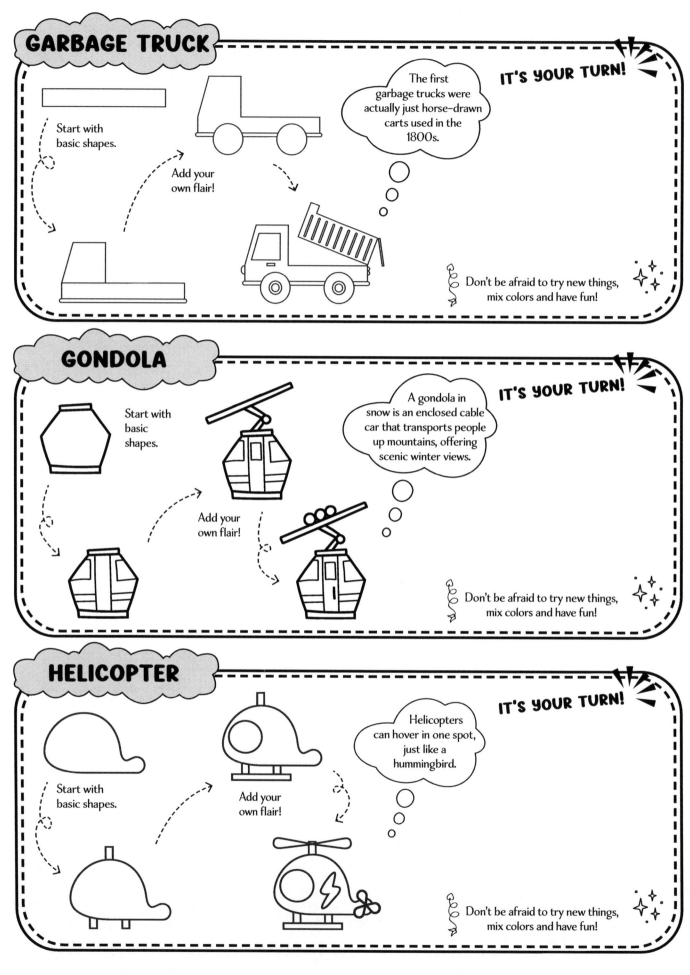

GARBAGE TRUCK

Start with basic shapes.

Add your own flair!

The first garbage trucks were actually just horse-drawn carts used in the 1800s.

IT'S YOUR TURN!

Don't be afraid to try new things, mix colors and have fun!

GONDOLA

Start with basic shapes.

Add your own flair!

A gondola in snow is an enclosed cable car that transports people up mountains, offering scenic winter views.

IT'S YOUR TURN!

Don't be afraid to try new things, mix colors and have fun!

HELICOPTER

Start with basic shapes.

Add your own flair!

Helicopters can hover in one spot, just like a hummingbird.

IT'S YOUR TURN!

Don't be afraid to try new things, mix colors and have fun!

52

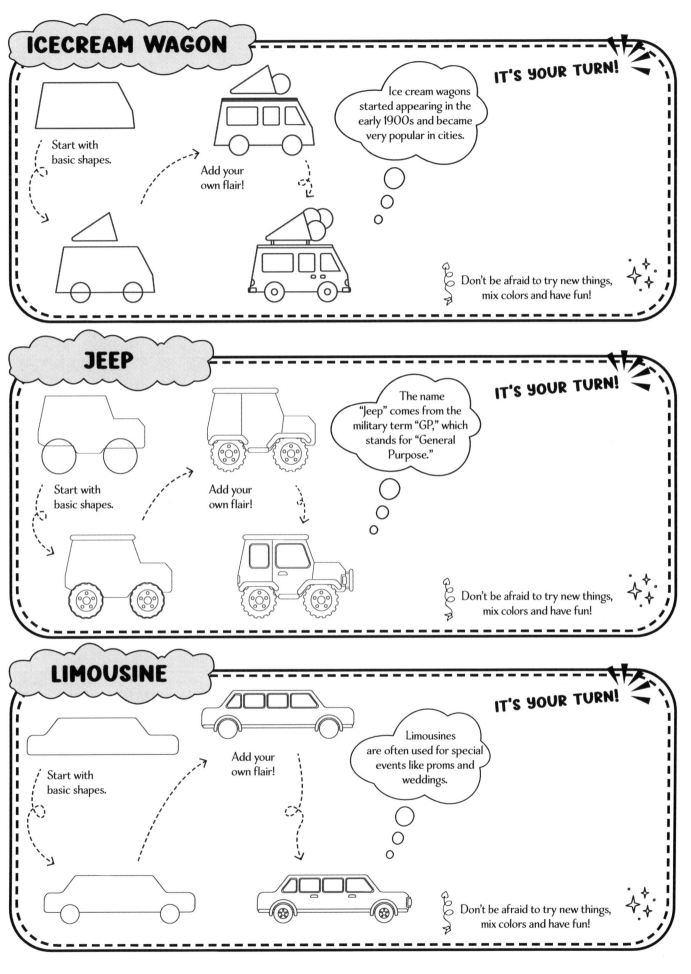

LORRY

Start with basic shapes.

Add your own flair!

The word "lorry" is British and means the same thing as "truck" in American English.

IT'S YOUR TURN!

Don't be afraid to try new things, mix colors and have fun!

MINI BUS

Start with basic shapes.

Add your own flair!

Mini buses are often used for tours and can navigate narrow streets better than large buses.

IT'S YOUR TURN!

Don't be afraid to try new things, mix colors and have fun!

MINIVAN

Start with basic shapes.

Add your own flair!

Minivans became popular in the 1980s as a family-friendly vehicle.

IT'S YOUR TURN!

Don't be afraid to try new things, mix colors and have fun!

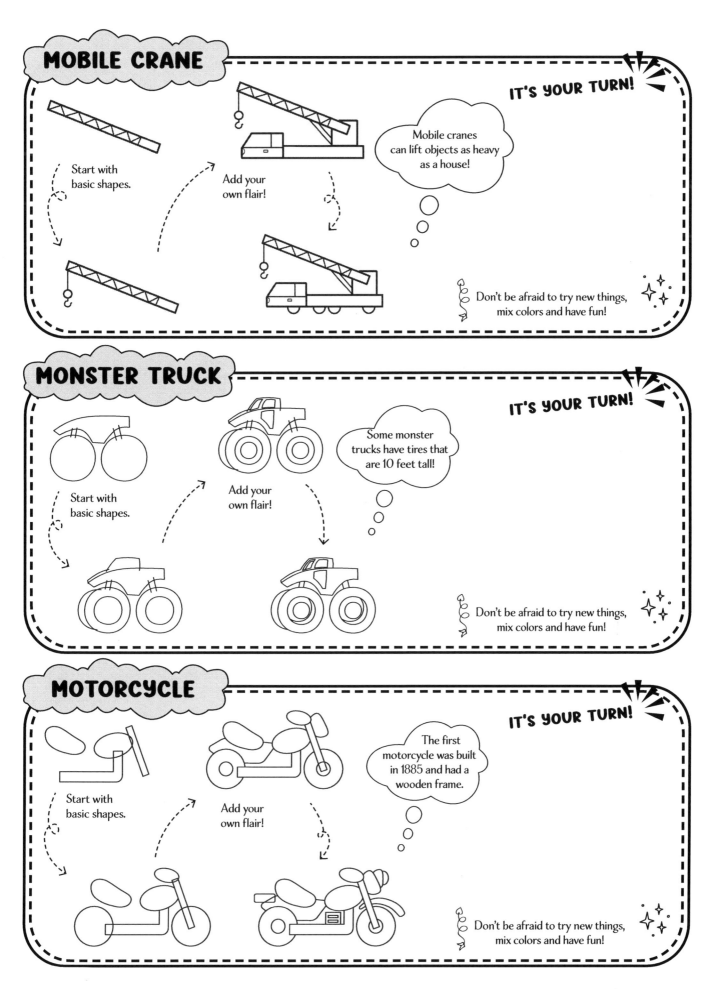

MOBILE CRANE

IT'S YOUR TURN!

Start with basic shapes.

Add your own flair!

Mobile cranes can lift objects as heavy as a house!

Don't be afraid to try new things, mix colors and have fun!

MONSTER TRUCK

IT'S YOUR TURN!

Start with basic shapes.

Add your own flair!

Some monster trucks have tires that are 10 feet tall!

Don't be afraid to try new things, mix colors and have fun!

MOTORCYCLE

IT'S YOUR TURN!

Start with basic shapes.

Add your own flair!

The first motorcycle was built in 1885 and had a wooden frame.

Don't be afraid to try new things, mix colors and have fun!

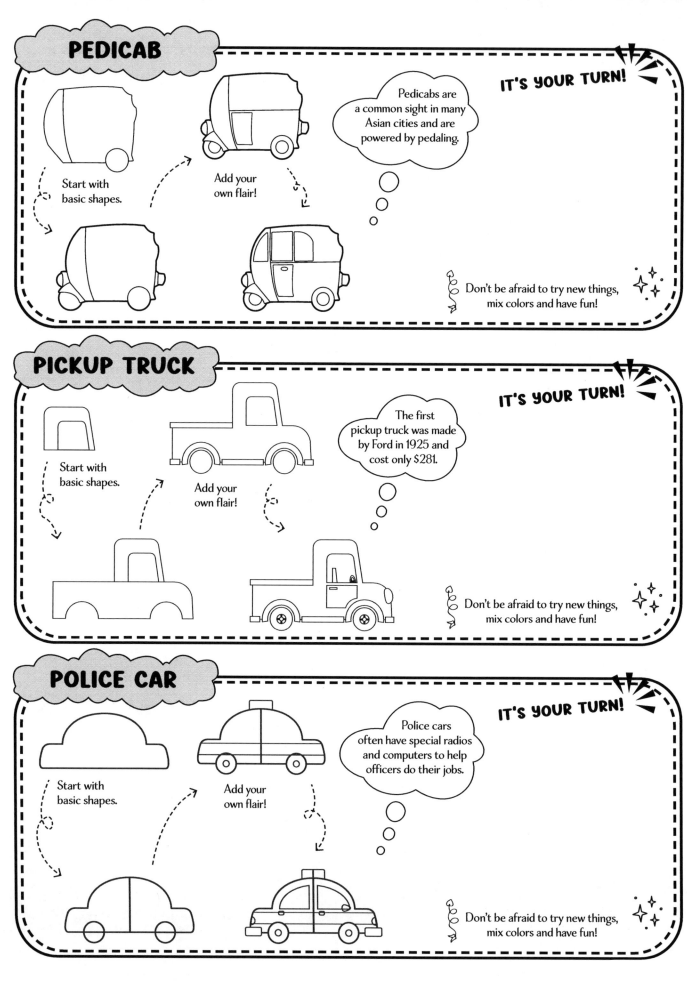

PEDICAB

IT'S YOUR TURN!

Start with basic shapes.

Add your own flair!

Pedicabs are a common sight in many Asian cities and are powered by pedaling.

Don't be afraid to try new things, mix colors and have fun!

PICKUP TRUCK

IT'S YOUR TURN!

Start with basic shapes.

Add your own flair!

The first pickup truck was made by Ford in 1925 and cost only $281.

Don't be afraid to try new things, mix colors and have fun!

POLICE CAR

IT'S YOUR TURN!

Start with basic shapes.

Add your own flair!

Police cars often have special radios and computers to help officers do their jobs.

Don't be afraid to try new things, mix colors and have fun!

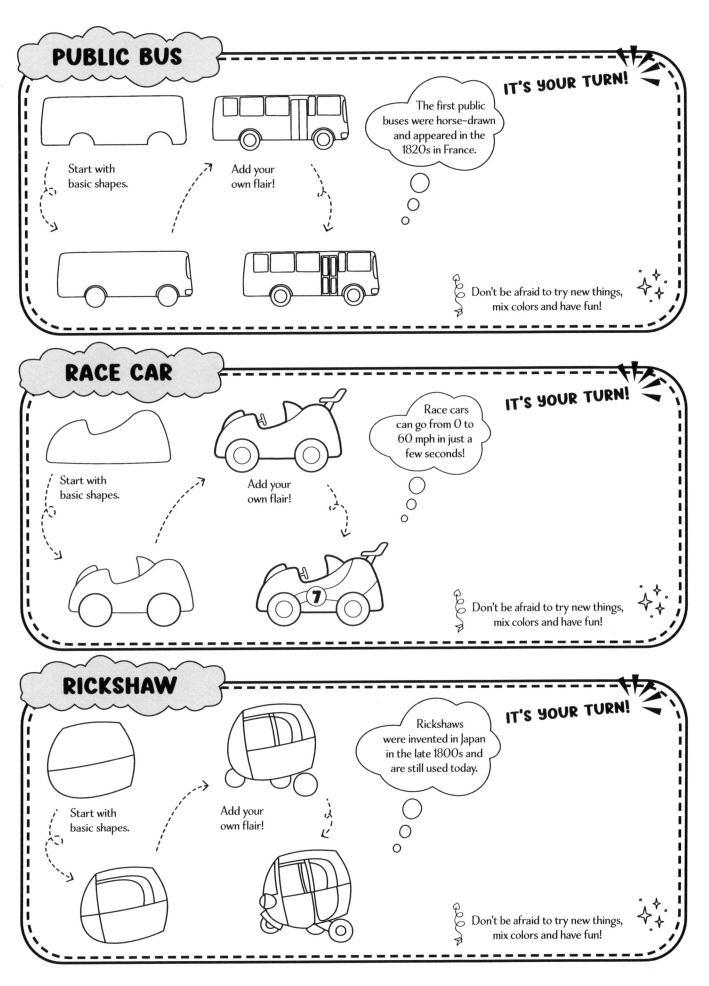

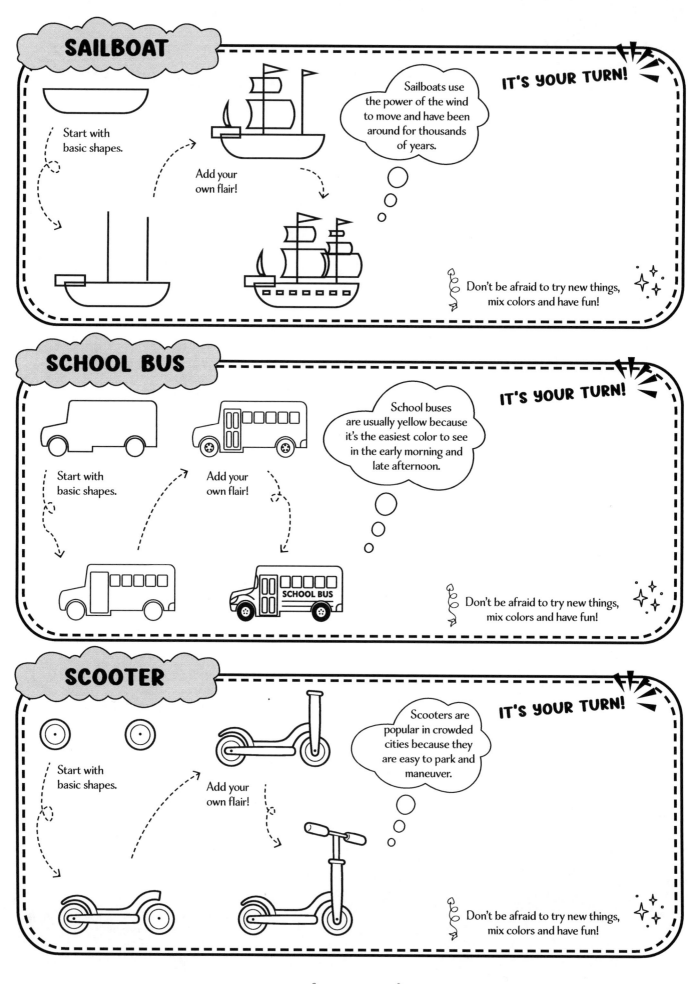

SAILBOAT

Start with basic shapes.

Add your own flair!

Sailboats use the power of the wind to move and have been around for thousands of years.

IT'S YOUR TURN!

Don't be afraid to try new things, mix colors and have fun!

SCHOOL BUS

Start with basic shapes.

Add your own flair!

School buses are usually yellow because it's the easiest color to see in the early morning and late afternoon.

IT'S YOUR TURN!

SCHOOL BUS

Don't be afraid to try new things, mix colors and have fun!

SCOOTER

Start with basic shapes.

Add your own flair!

Scooters are popular in crowded cities because they are easy to park and maneuver.

IT'S YOUR TURN!

Don't be afraid to try new things, mix colors and have fun!

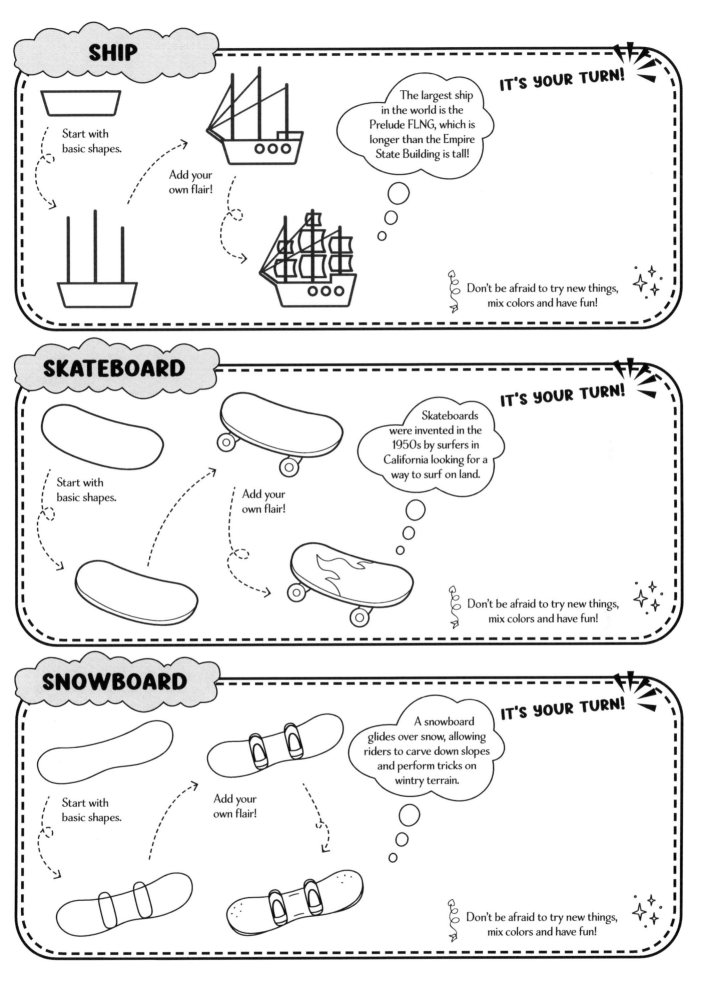

SHIP

Start with basic shapes.

Add your own flair!

The largest ship in the world is the Prelude FLNG, which is longer than the Empire State Building is tall!

IT'S YOUR TURN!

Don't be afraid to try new things, mix colors and have fun!

SKATEBOARD

Start with basic shapes.

Add your own flair!

Skateboards were invented in the 1950s by surfers in California looking for a way to surf on land.

IT'S YOUR TURN!

Don't be afraid to try new things, mix colors and have fun!

SNOWBOARD

Start with basic shapes.

Add your own flair!

A snowboard glides over snow, allowing riders to carve down slopes and perform tricks on wintry terrain.

IT'S YOUR TURN!

Don't be afraid to try new things, mix colors and have fun!

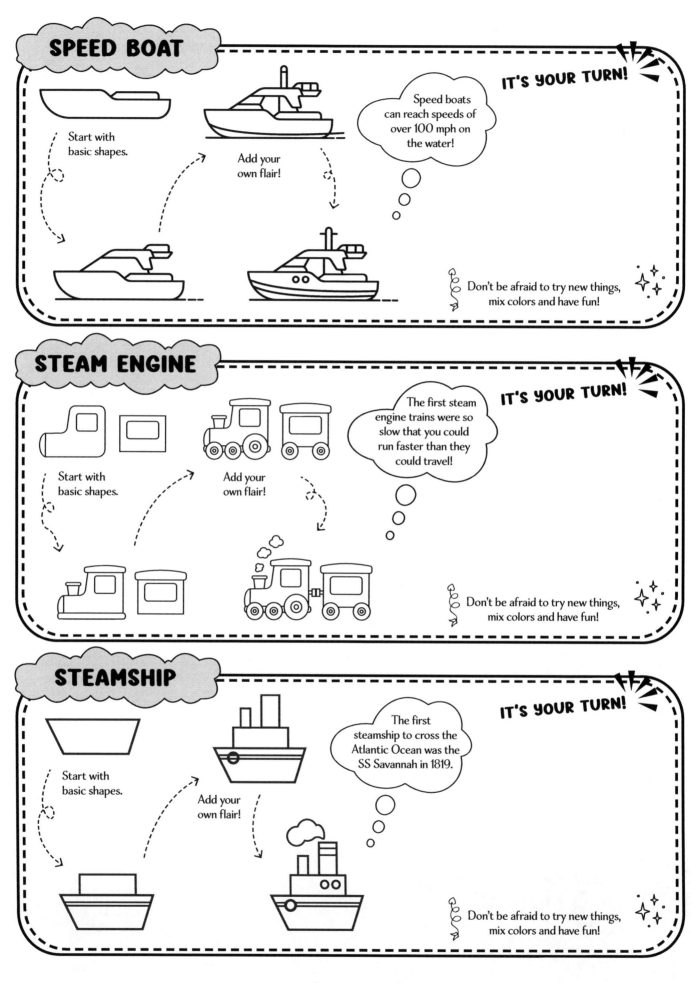

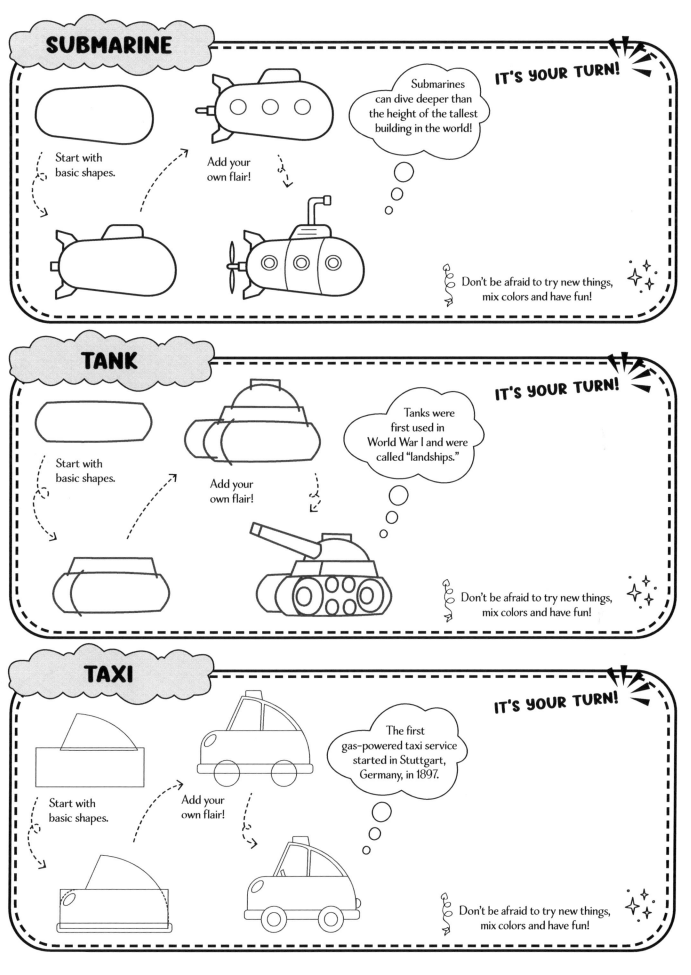

SUBMARINE

Start with basic shapes.

Add your own flair!

IT'S YOUR TURN!

Submarines can dive deeper than the height of the tallest building in the world!

Don't be afraid to try new things, mix colors and have fun!

TANK

Start with basic shapes.

Add your own flair!

IT'S YOUR TURN!

Tanks were first used in World War I and were called "landships."

Don't be afraid to try new things, mix colors and have fun!

TAXI

Start with basic shapes.

Add your own flair!

IT'S YOUR TURN!

The first gas-powered taxi service started in Stuttgart, Germany, in 1897.

Don't be afraid to try new things, mix colors and have fun!

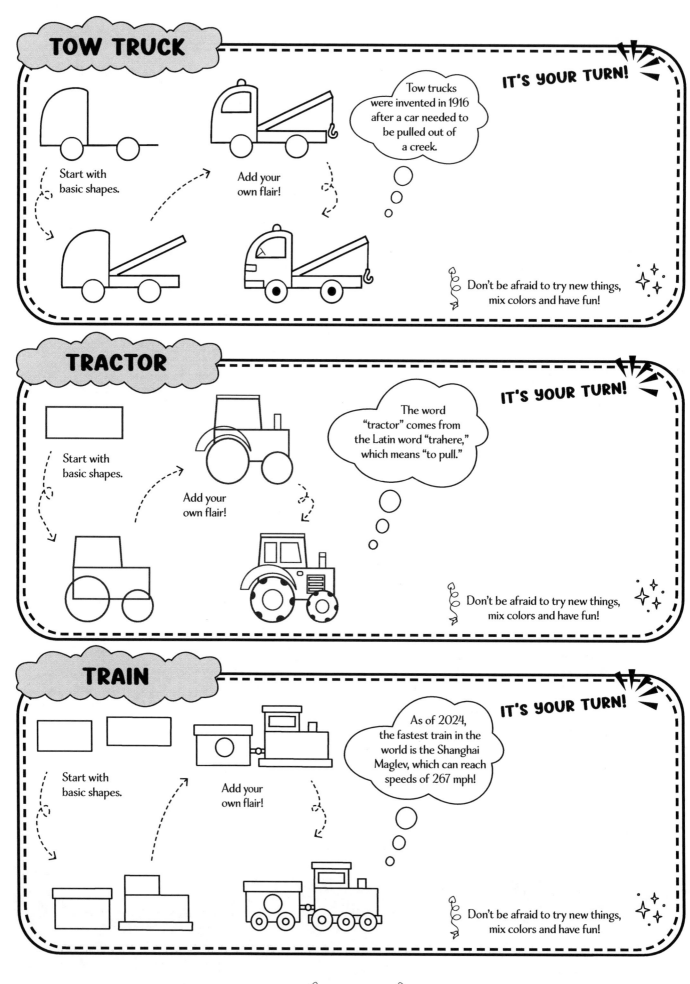

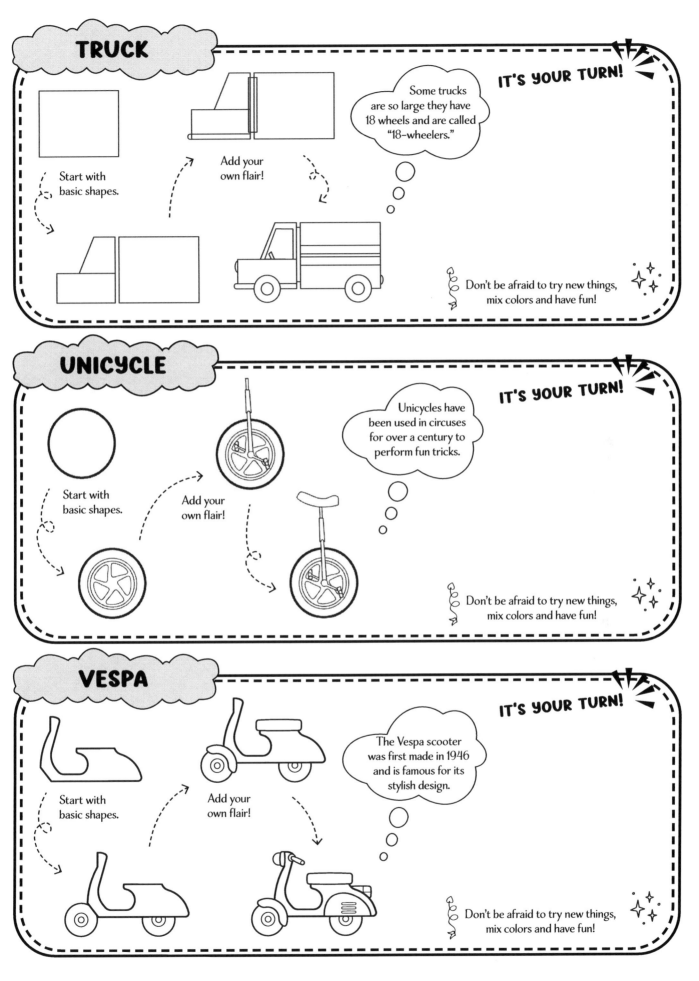

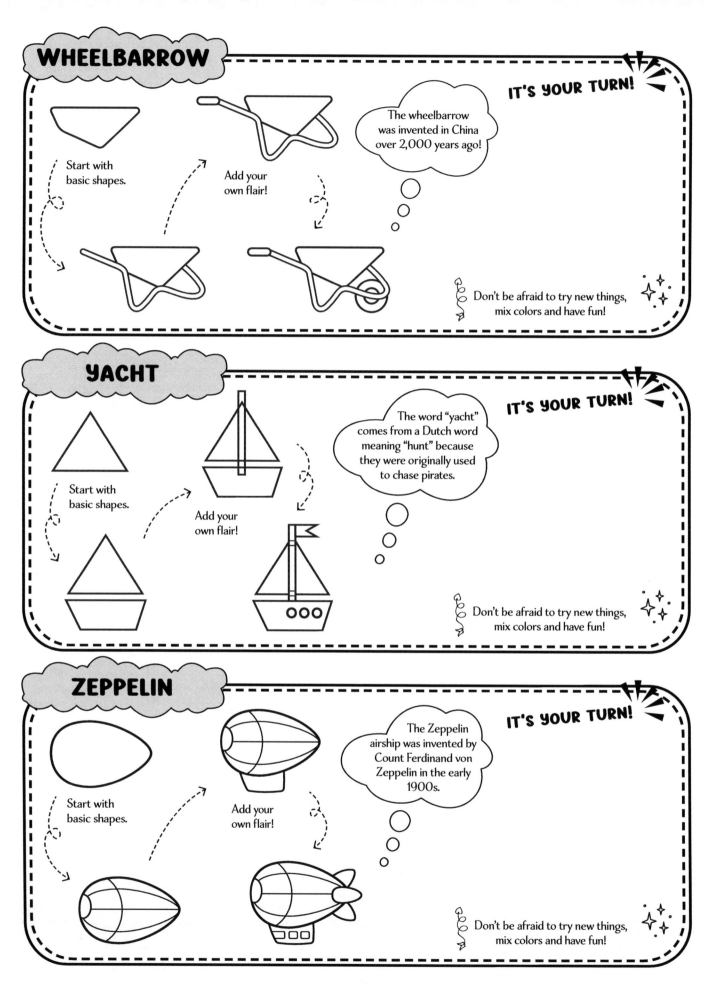

WHEELBARROW

Start with basic shapes.

Add your own flair!

The wheelbarrow was invented in China over 2,000 years ago!

IT'S YOUR TURN!

Don't be afraid to try new things, mix colors and have fun!

YACHT

Start with basic shapes.

Add your own flair!

The word "yacht" comes from a Dutch word meaning "hunt" because they were originally used to chase pirates.

IT'S YOUR TURN!

Don't be afraid to try new things, mix colors and have fun!

ZEPPELIN

Start with basic shapes.

Add your own flair!

The Zeppelin airship was invented by Count Ferdinand von Zeppelin in the early 1900s.

IT'S YOUR TURN!

Don't be afraid to try new things, mix colors and have fun!

Fantasy and Adventure

> Bring us to life with your colors!

Ever seen an **Ouranosaurus**, a **UFO**, or a **Fairy**? Maybe not, because some of these are **fantasy**, some are rare, and some are extinct! But don't worry—this chapter will guide you on an adventure to bring them to life on paper!

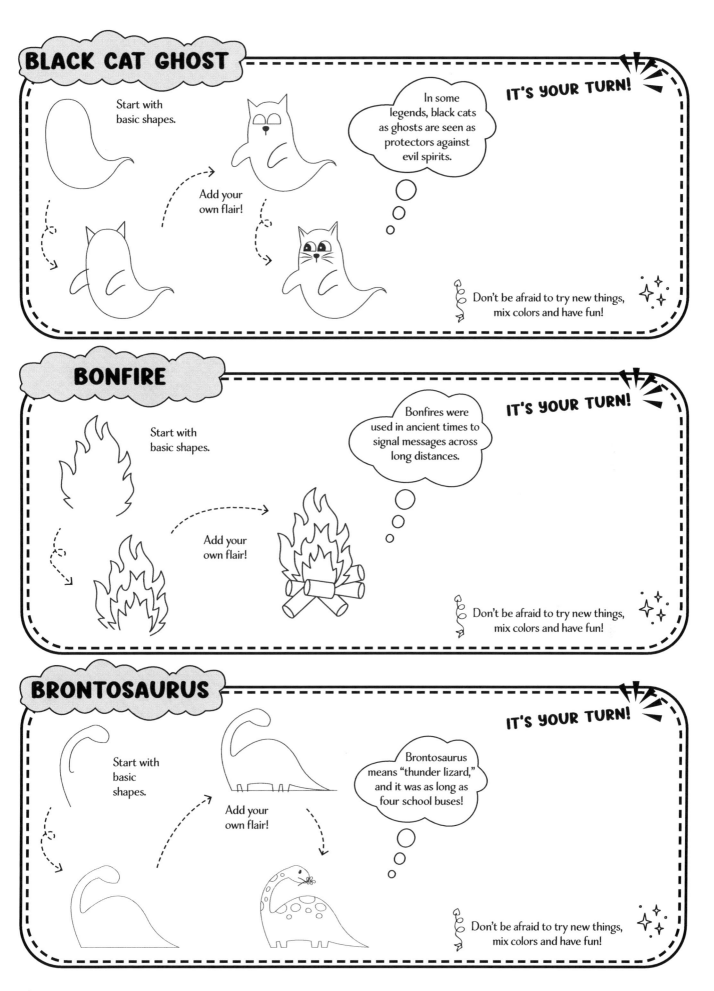

67

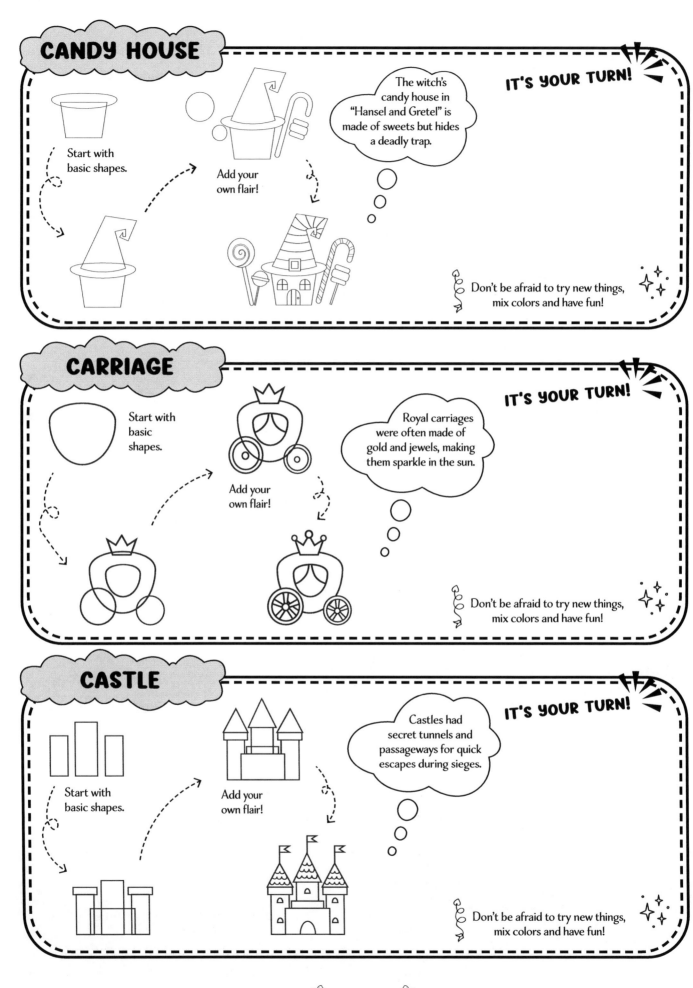

CANDY HOUSE

IT'S YOUR TURN!

Start with basic shapes.

Add your own flair!

The witch's candy house in "Hansel and Gretel" is made of sweets but hides a deadly trap.

Don't be afraid to try new things, mix colors and have fun!

CARRIAGE

IT'S YOUR TURN!

Start with basic shapes.

Add your own flair!

Royal carriages were often made of gold and jewels, making them sparkle in the sun.

Don't be afraid to try new things, mix colors and have fun!

CASTLE

IT'S YOUR TURN!

Start with basic shapes.

Add your own flair!

Castles had secret tunnels and passageways for quick escapes during sieges.

Don't be afraid to try new things, mix colors and have fun!

CROWN

Start with basic shapes.

Add your own flair!

Crowns have been used for thousands of years to show royalty and power.

IT'S YOUR TURN!

Don't be afraid to try new things, mix colors and have fun!

DINOSAUR

Start with basic shapes.

Add your own flair!

Dinosaurs lived on Earth millions of years before humans existed!

IT'S YOUR TURN!

Don't be afraid to try new things, mix colors and have fun!

DRAGON

Start with basic shapes.

Add your own flair!

Dragons appear in myths worldwide, often guarding treasure and breathing fire.

IT'S YOUR TURN!

Don't be afraid to try new things, mix colors and have fun!

EASTER BASKET

Start with basic shapes.

Add your own flair!

The tradition of Easter baskets comes from the idea of giving gifts in a bird's nest.

IT'S YOUR TURN!

Don't be afraid to try new things, mix colors and have fun!

EASTER BUNNY

Start with basic shapes.

Add your own flair!

The Easter Bunny originated from a German tradition about a hare bringing eggs.

IT'S YOUR TURN!

Don't be afraid to try new things, mix colors and have fun!

EASTER EGG

Start with basic shapes.

Add your own flair!

Easter eggs symbolize new life and rebirth, celebrated during spring.

IT'S YOUR TURN!

Don't be afraid to try new things, mix colors and have fun!

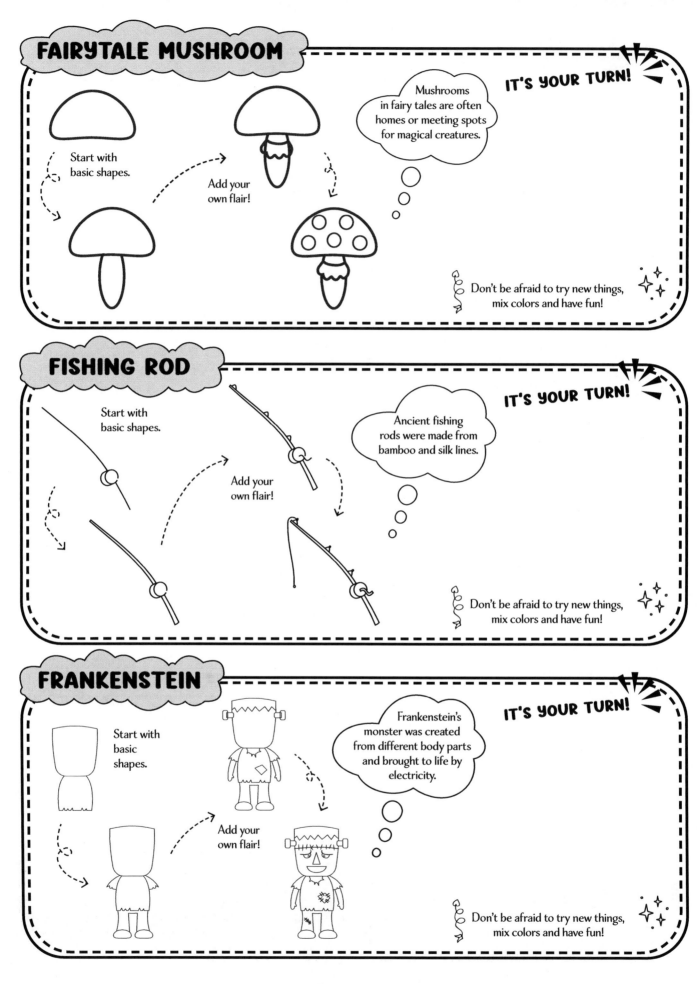

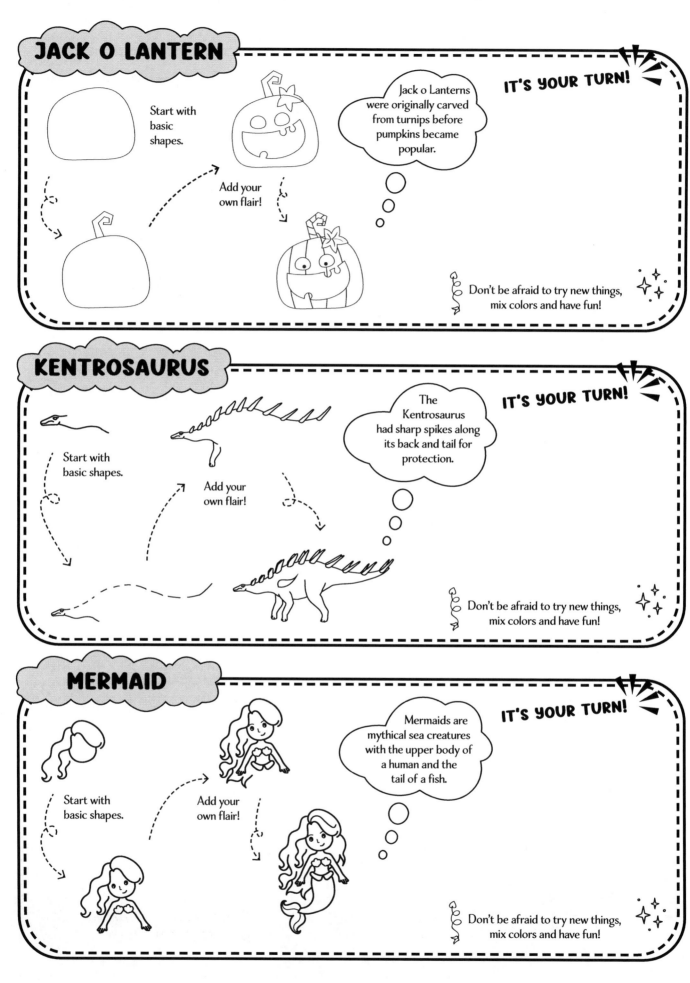

MONSTER

Start with basic shapes.

Add your own flair!

Fantasy monsters symbolize challenges that heroes must overcome.

IT'S YOUR TURN!

Don't be afraid to try new things, mix colors and have fun!

MUMMY GHOST

Start with basic shapes.

Add your own flair!

Mummies were preserved with special techniques to last for thousands of years.

IT'S YOUR TURN!

Don't be afraid to try new things, mix colors and have fun!

MUSHROOM HOUSE

Start with basic shapes.

Add your own flair!

In stories, mushroom houses are often homes to fairies and other magical beings.

IT'S YOUR TURN!

Don't be afraid to try new things, mix colors and have fun!

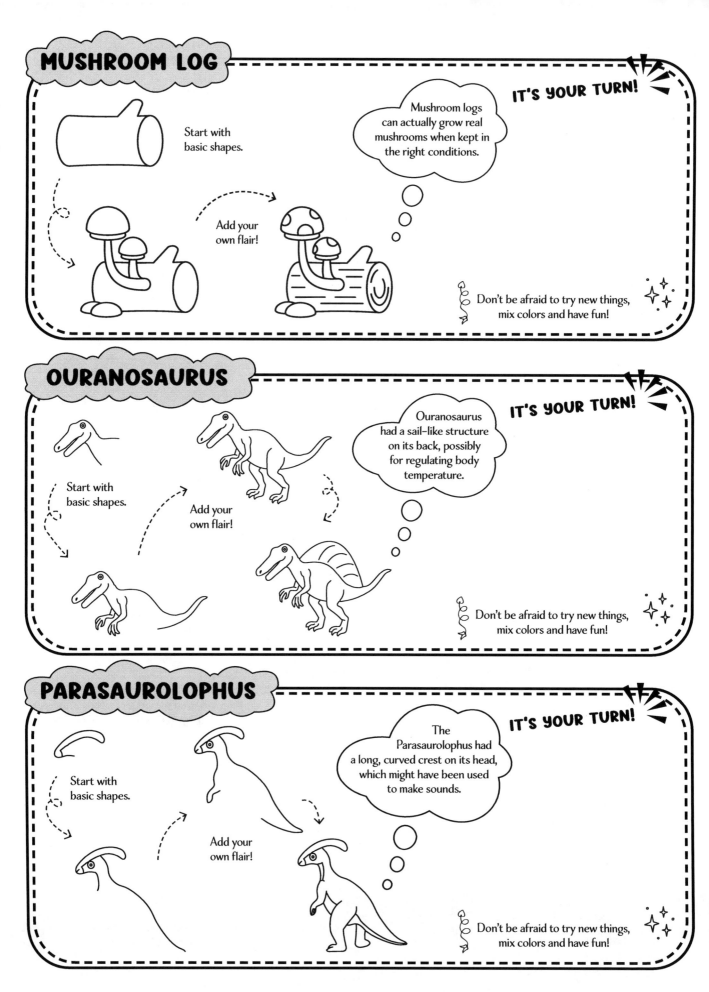

MUSHROOM LOG

Start with basic shapes.

Add your own flair!

Mushroom logs can actually grow real mushrooms when kept in the right conditions.

IT'S YOUR TURN!

Don't be afraid to try new things, mix colors and have fun!

OURANOSAURUS

Start with basic shapes.

Add your own flair!

Ouranosaurus had a sail-like structure on its back, possibly for regulating body temperature.

IT'S YOUR TURN!

Don't be afraid to try new things, mix colors and have fun!

PARASAUROLOPHUS

Start with basic shapes.

Add your own flair!

The Parasaurolophus had a long, curved crest on its head, which might have been used to make sounds.

IT'S YOUR TURN!

Don't be afraid to try new things, mix colors and have fun!

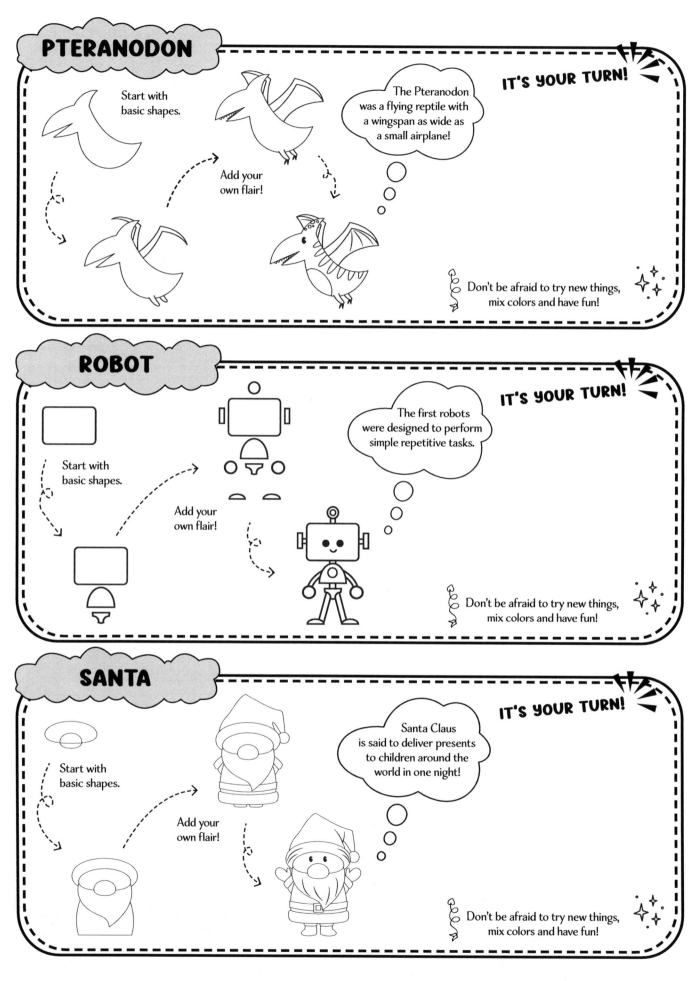

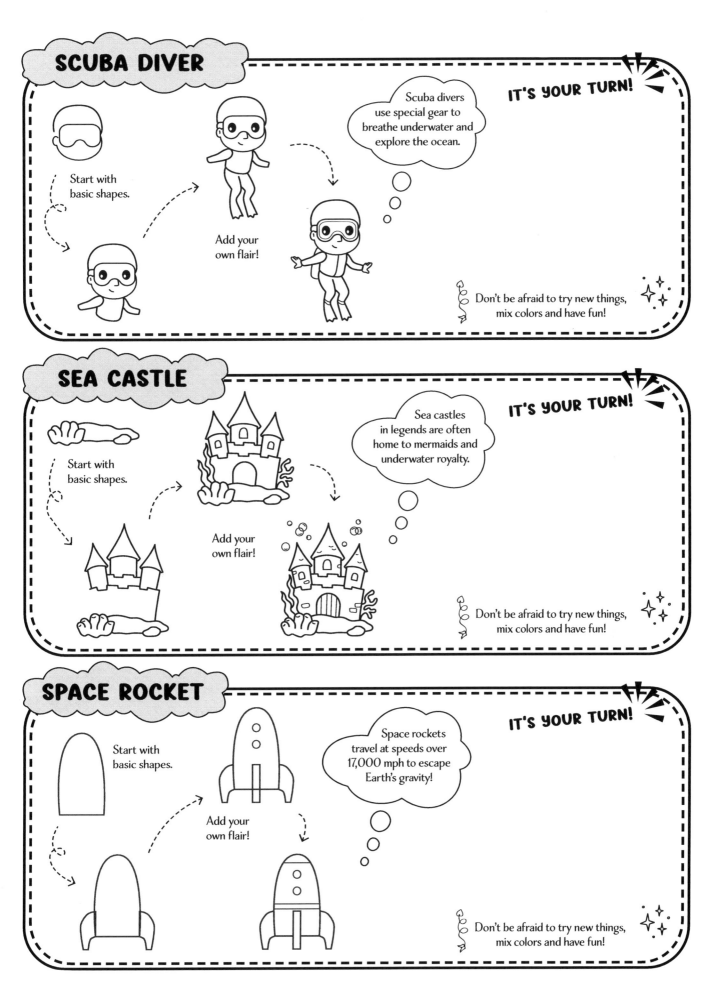

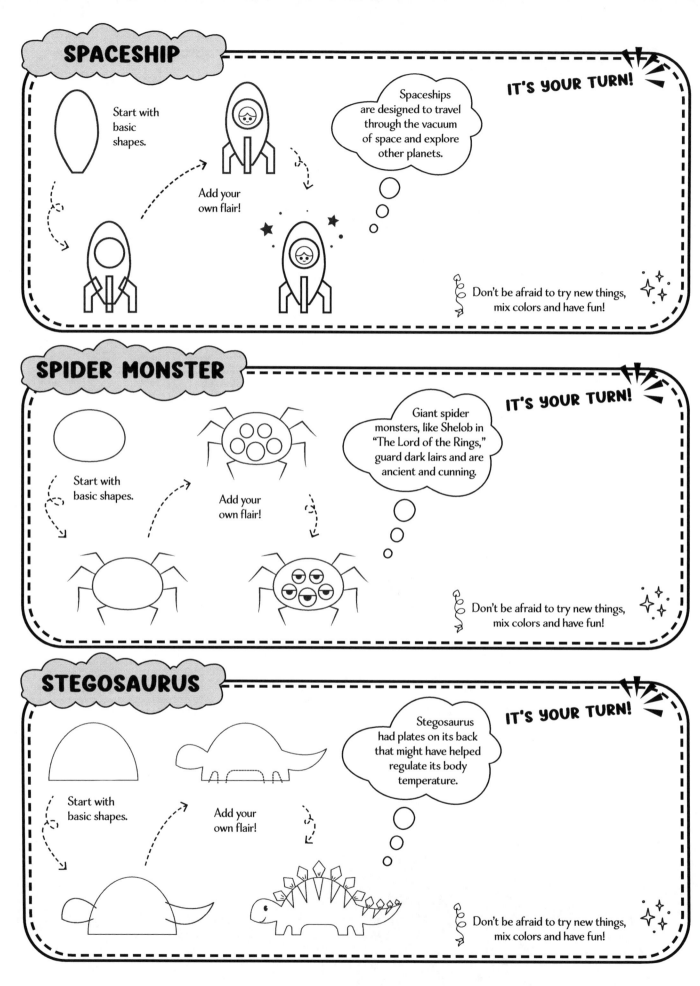

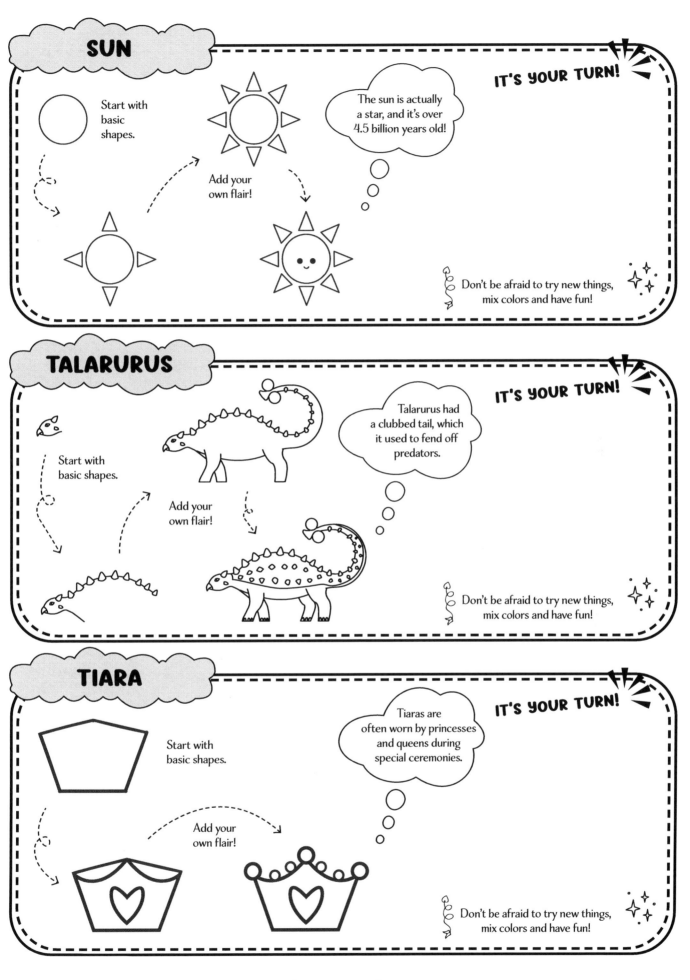

SUN

Start with basic shapes.

Add your own flair!

The sun is actually a star, and it's over 4.5 billion years old!

IT'S YOUR TURN!

Don't be afraid to try new things, mix colors and have fun!

TALARURUS

Start with basic shapes.

Add your own flair!

Talarurus had a clubbed tail, which it used to fend off predators.

IT'S YOUR TURN!

Don't be afraid to try new things, mix colors and have fun!

TIARA

Start with basic shapes.

Add your own flair!

Tiaras are often worn by princesses and queens during special ceremonies.

IT'S YOUR TURN!

Don't be afraid to try new things, mix colors and have fun!

81

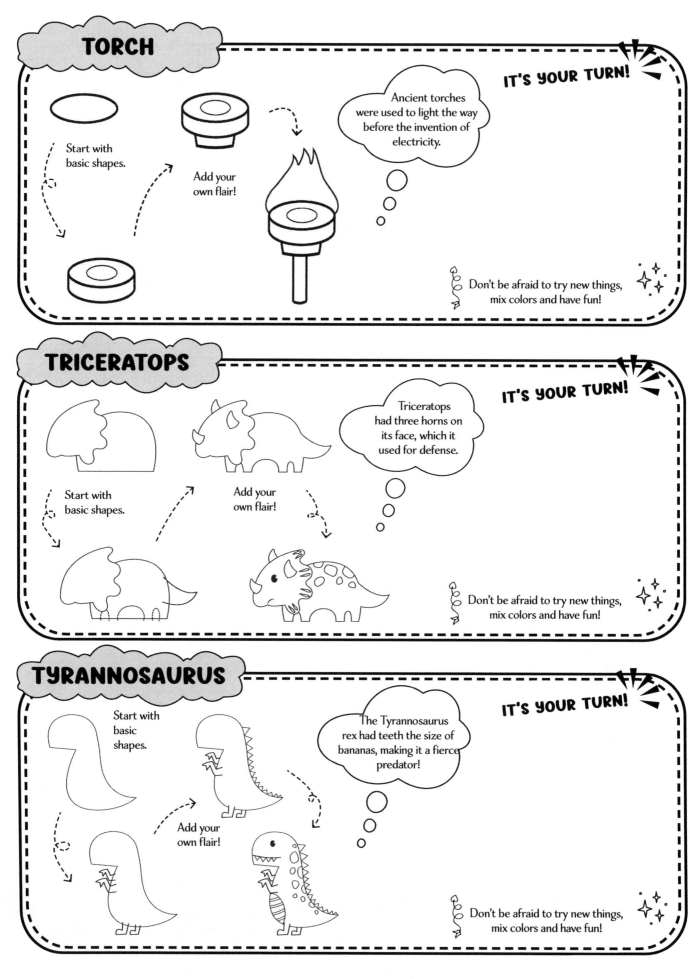

82

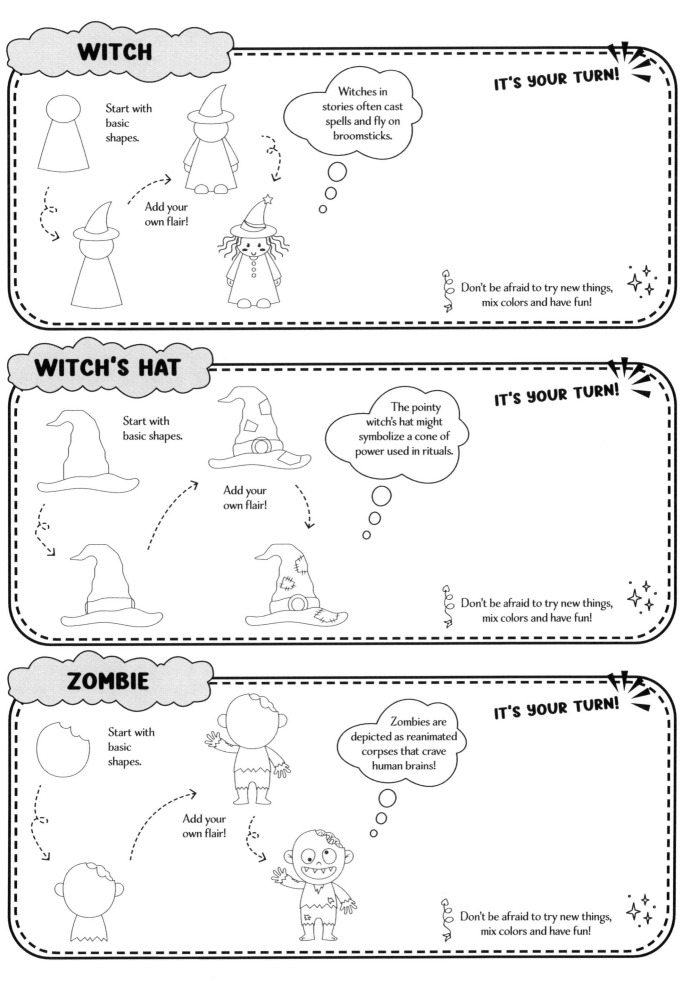

WITCH

Start with basic shapes.

Add your own flair!

Witches in stories often cast spells and fly on broomsticks.

IT'S YOUR TURN!

Don't be afraid to try new things, mix colors and have fun!

WITCH'S HAT

Start with basic shapes.

Add your own flair!

The pointy witch's hat might symbolize a cone of power used in rituals.

IT'S YOUR TURN!

Don't be afraid to try new things, mix colors and have fun!

ZOMBIE

Start with basic shapes.

Add your own flair!

Zombies are depicted as reanimated corpses that crave human brains!

IT'S YOUR TURN!

Don't be afraid to try new things, mix colors and have fun!

Everyday Objects

Bring us to life with your colors!

Drawing everyday **objects** is one way to **challenge yourself**. Why would that be **challenging?** Because it makes you pay attention to the things around you, like the **pencil** you are using or the **light bulb** in your **room**. Try the activities in this chapter and draw the things that can be found almost anywhere.

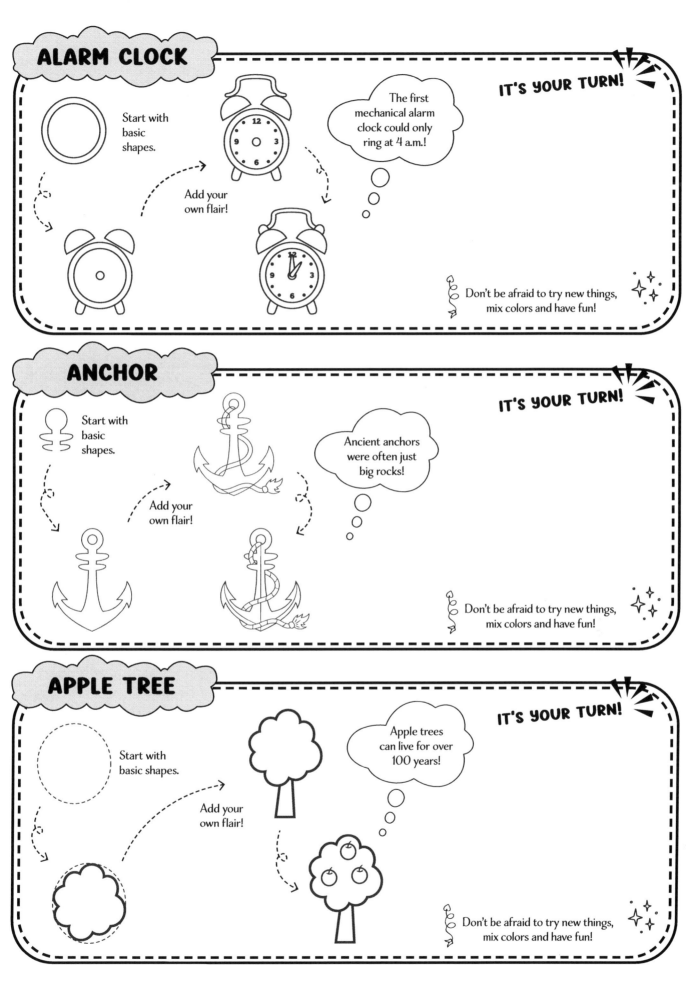

ALARM CLOCK

IT'S YOUR TURN!

Start with basic shapes.

Add your own flair!

The first mechanical alarm clock could only ring at 4 a.m.!

Don't be afraid to try new things, mix colors and have fun!

ANCHOR

IT'S YOUR TURN!

Start with basic shapes.

Add your own flair!

Ancient anchors were often just big rocks!

Don't be afraid to try new things, mix colors and have fun!

APPLE TREE

IT'S YOUR TURN!

Start with basic shapes.

Add your own flair!

Apple trees can live for over 100 years!

Don't be afraid to try new things, mix colors and have fun!

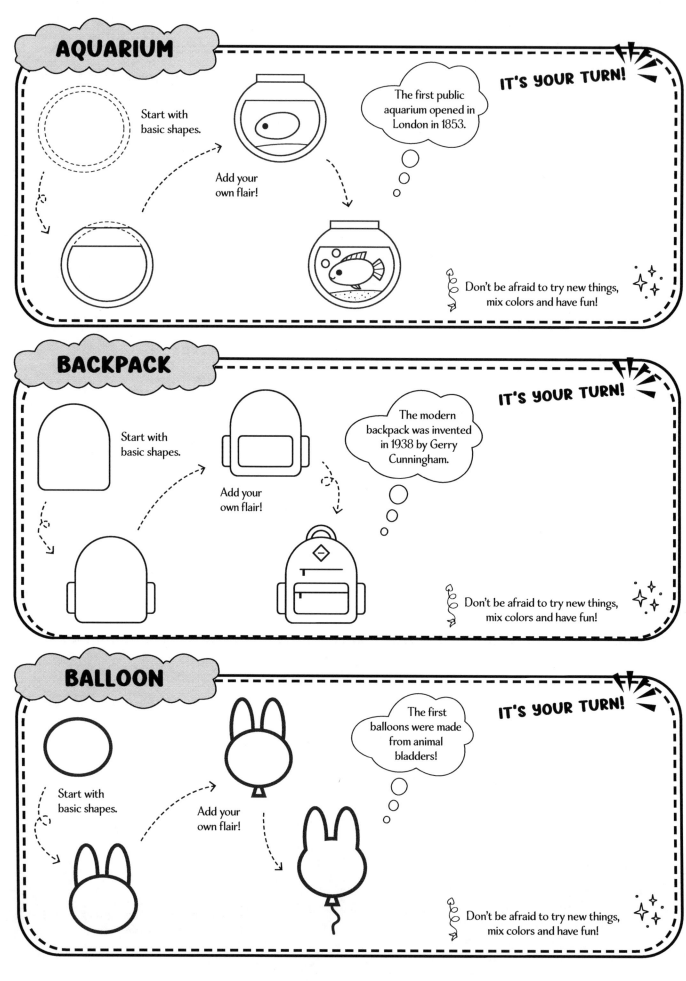

AQUARIUM

Start with basic shapes.

Add your own flair!

The first public aquarium opened in London in 1853.

IT'S YOUR TURN!

Don't be afraid to try new things, mix colors and have fun!

BACKPACK

Start with basic shapes.

Add your own flair!

The modern backpack was invented in 1938 by Gerry Cunningham.

IT'S YOUR TURN!

Don't be afraid to try new things, mix colors and have fun!

BALLOON

Start with basic shapes.

Add your own flair!

The first balloons were made from animal bladders!

IT'S YOUR TURN!

Don't be afraid to try new things, mix colors and have fun!

BATH SPONGE

Start with basic shapes.

Add your own flair!

A bath sponge makes bubbles and fun times!

IT'S YOUR TURN!

Don't be afraid to try new things, mix colors and have fun!

BEACH BALL

Start with basic shapes.

Add your own flair!

The largest beach ball ever made was over 65 feet in diameter!

IT'S YOUR TURN!

Don't be afraid to try new things, mix colors and have fun!

BOOK

Start with basic shapes.

Add your own flair!

The longest book ever written is "In Search of Lost Time" by Proust.

IT'S YOUR TURN!

Don't be afraid to try new things, mix colors and have fun!

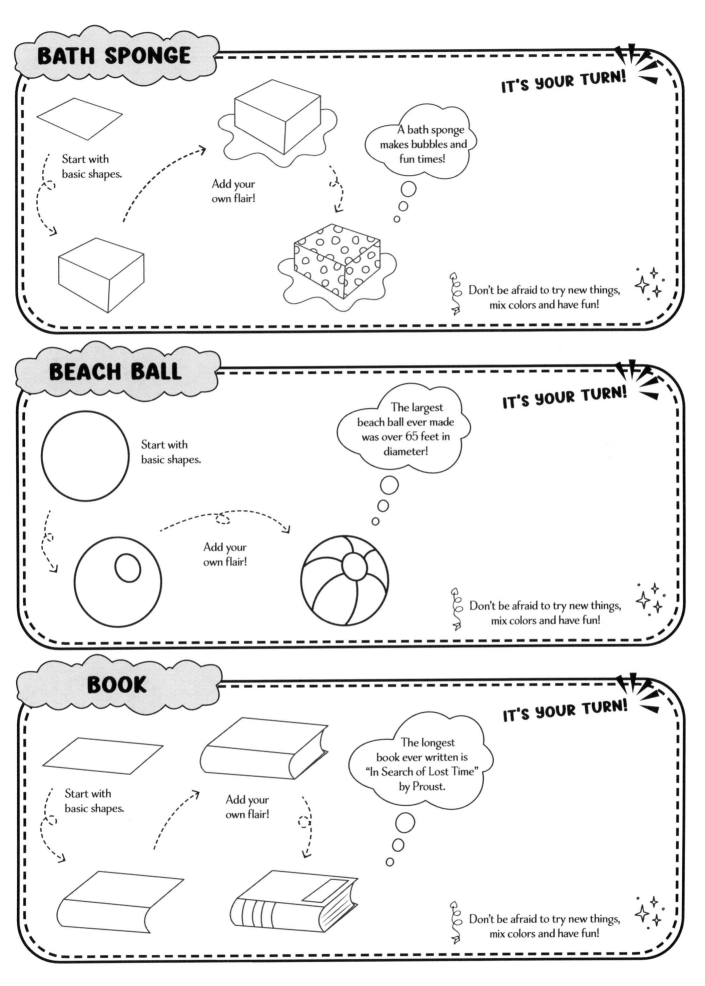

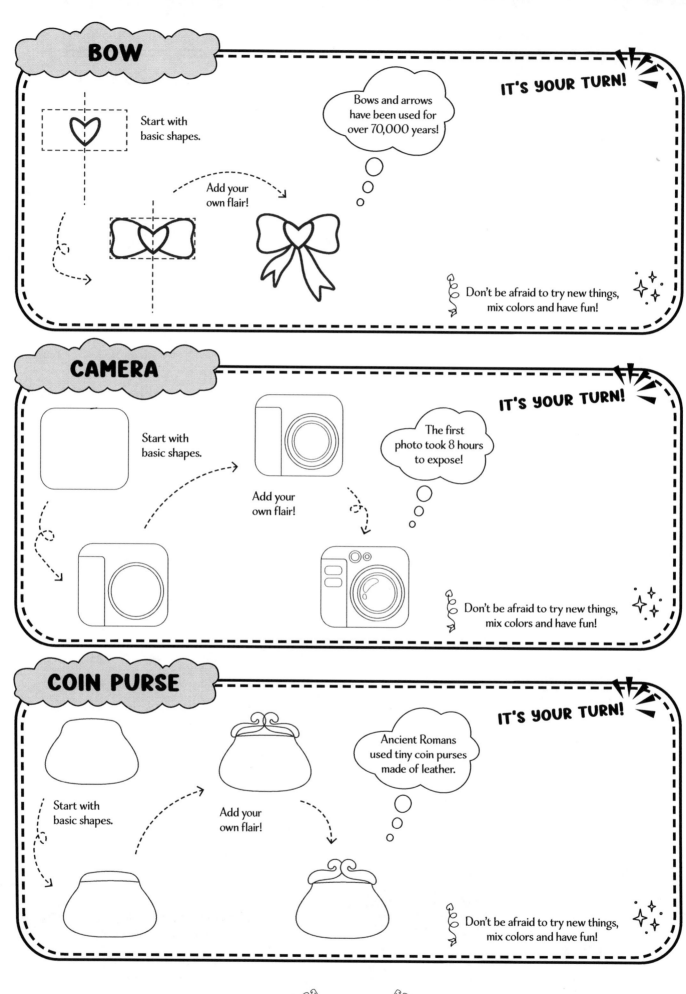

BOW

Start with basic shapes.

Add your own flair!

Bows and arrows have been used for over 70,000 years!

IT'S YOUR TURN!

Don't be afraid to try new things, mix colors and have fun!

CAMERA

Start with basic shapes.

Add your own flair!

The first photo took 8 hours to expose!

IT'S YOUR TURN!

Don't be afraid to try new things, mix colors and have fun!

COIN PURSE

Start with basic shapes.

Add your own flair!

Ancient Romans used tiny coin purses made of leather.

IT'S YOUR TURN!

Don't be afraid to try new things, mix colors and have fun!

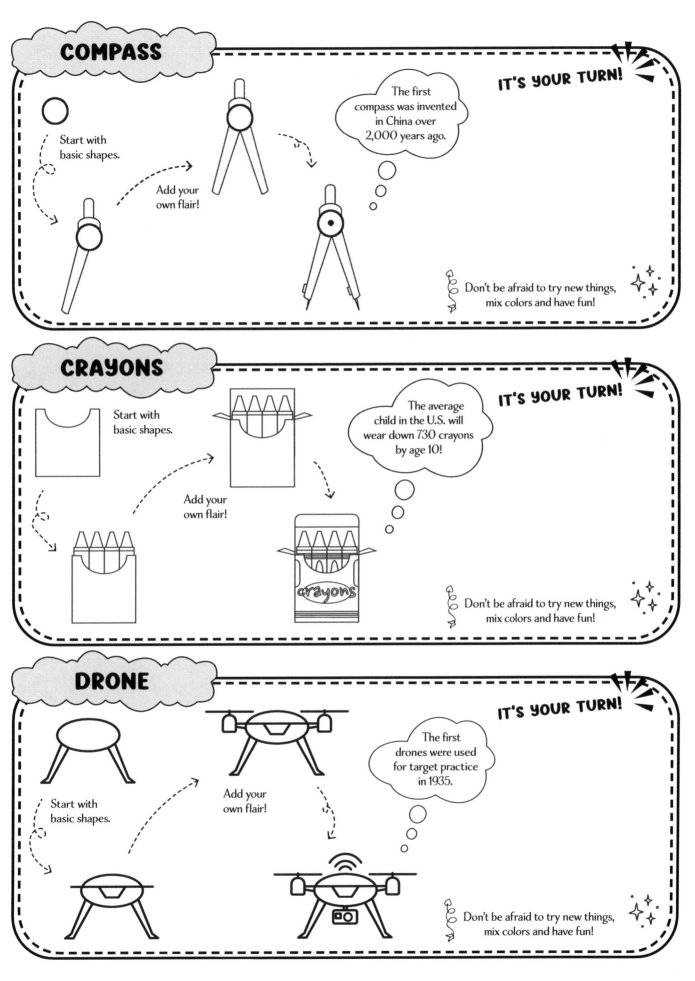

COMPASS

Start with basic shapes.

Add your own flair!

IT'S YOUR TURN!

The first compass was invented in China over 2,000 years ago.

Don't be afraid to try new things, mix colors and have fun!

CRAYONS

Start with basic shapes.

Add your own flair!

IT'S YOUR TURN!

The average child in the U.S. will wear down 730 crayons by age 10!

crayons

Don't be afraid to try new things, mix colors and have fun!

DRONE

Start with basic shapes.

Add your own flair!

IT'S YOUR TURN!

The first drones were used for target practice in 1935.

Don't be afraid to try new things, mix colors and have fun!

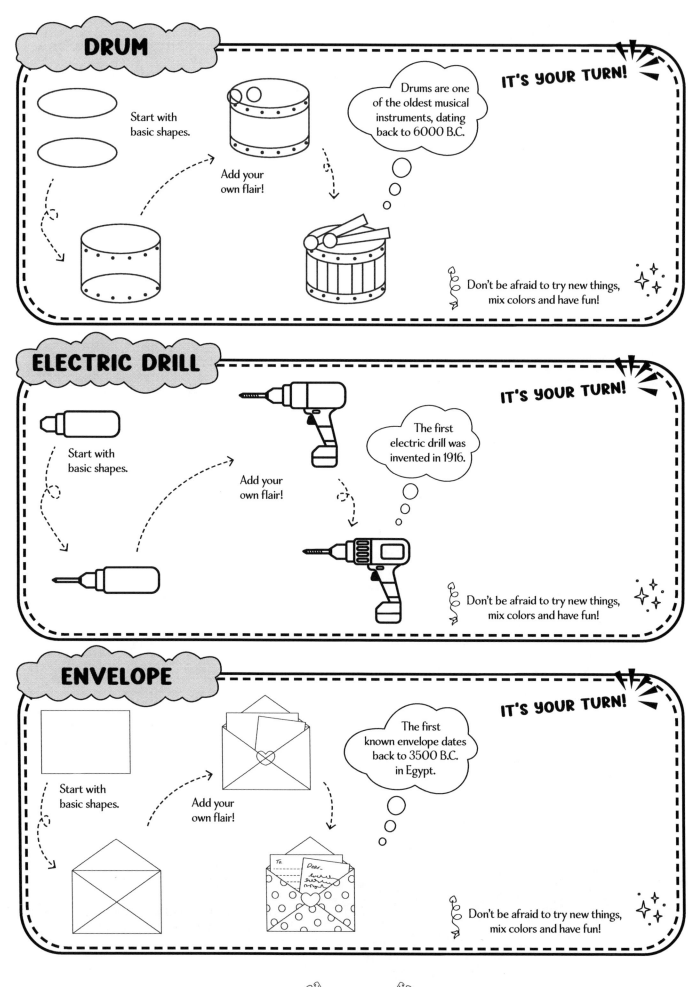

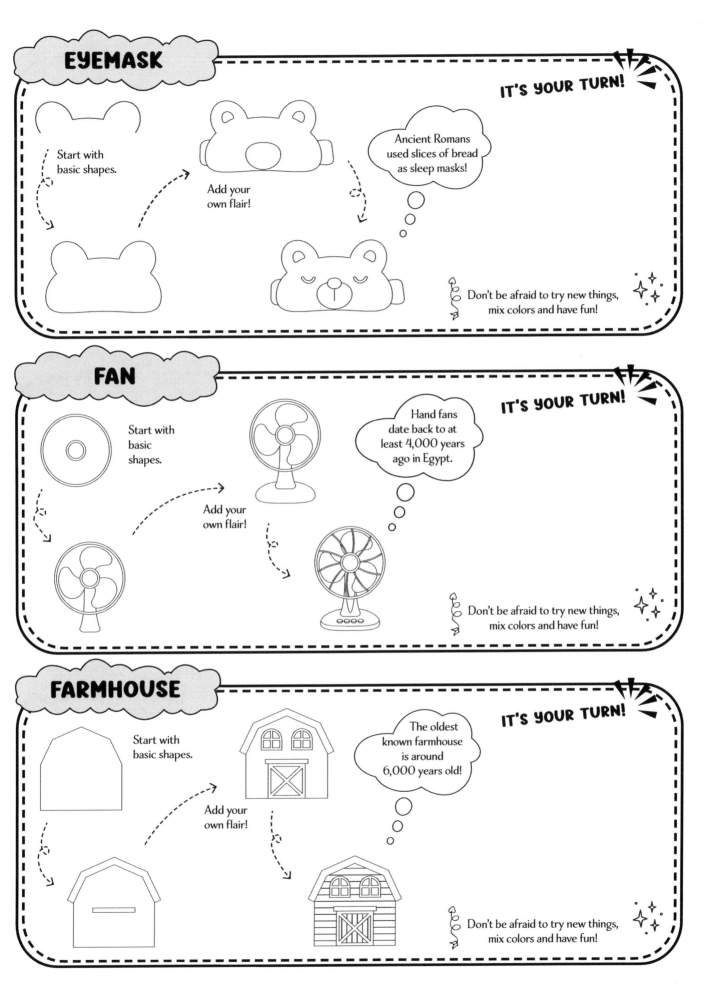

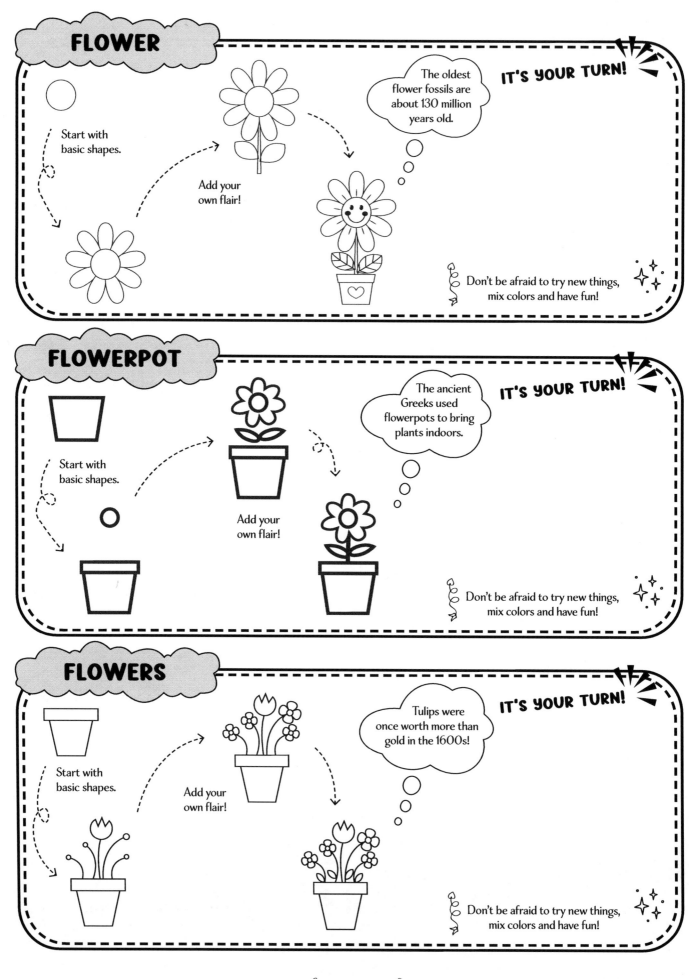

94

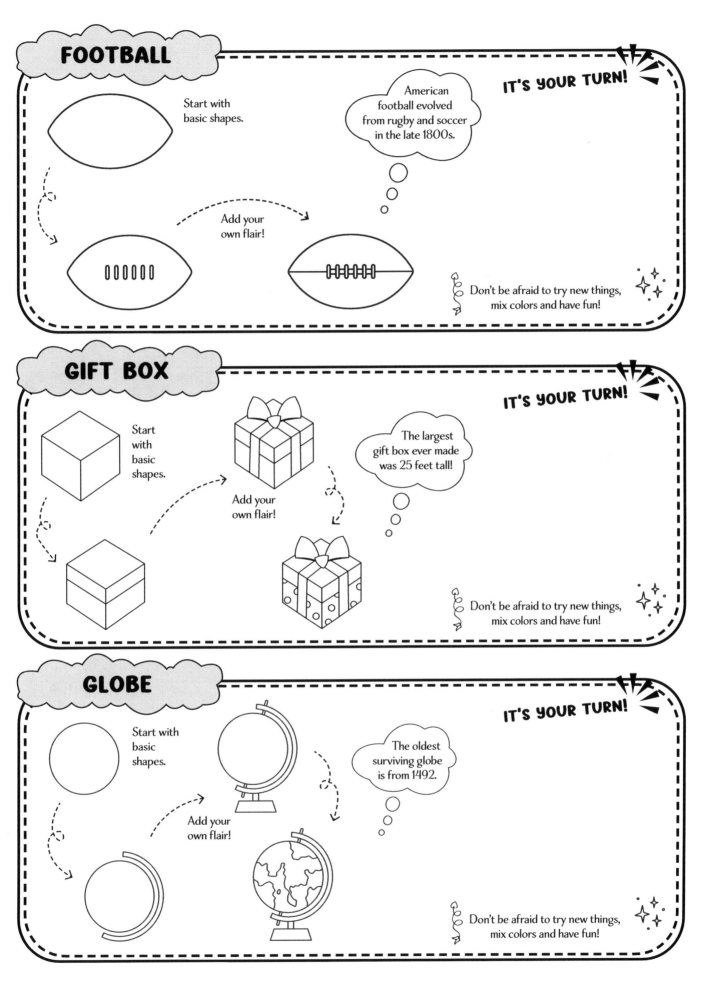

FOOTBALL

Start with basic shapes.

Add your own flair!

American football evolved from rugby and soccer in the late 1800s.

IT'S YOUR TURN!

Don't be afraid to try new things, mix colors and have fun!

GIFT BOX

Start with basic shapes.

Add your own flair!

The largest gift box ever made was 25 feet tall!

IT'S YOUR TURN!

Don't be afraid to try new things, mix colors and have fun!

GLOBE

Start with basic shapes.

Add your own flair!

The oldest surviving globe is from 1492.

IT'S YOUR TURN!

Don't be afraid to try new things, mix colors and have fun!

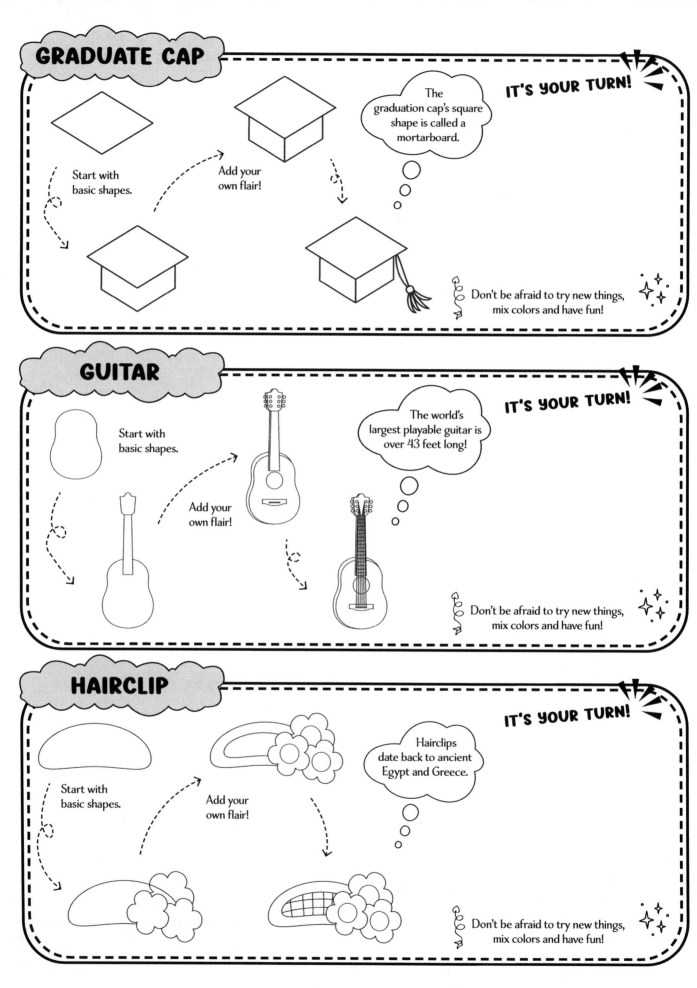

GRADUATE CAP

IT'S YOUR TURN!

Start with basic shapes.

Add your own flair!

The graduation cap's square shape is called a mortarboard.

Don't be afraid to try new things, mix colors and have fun!

GUITAR

IT'S YOUR TURN!

Start with basic shapes.

Add your own flair!

The world's largest playable guitar is over 43 feet long!

Don't be afraid to try new things, mix colors and have fun!

HAIRCLIP

IT'S YOUR TURN!

Start with basic shapes.

Add your own flair!

Hairclips date back to ancient Egypt and Greece.

Don't be afraid to try new things, mix colors and have fun!

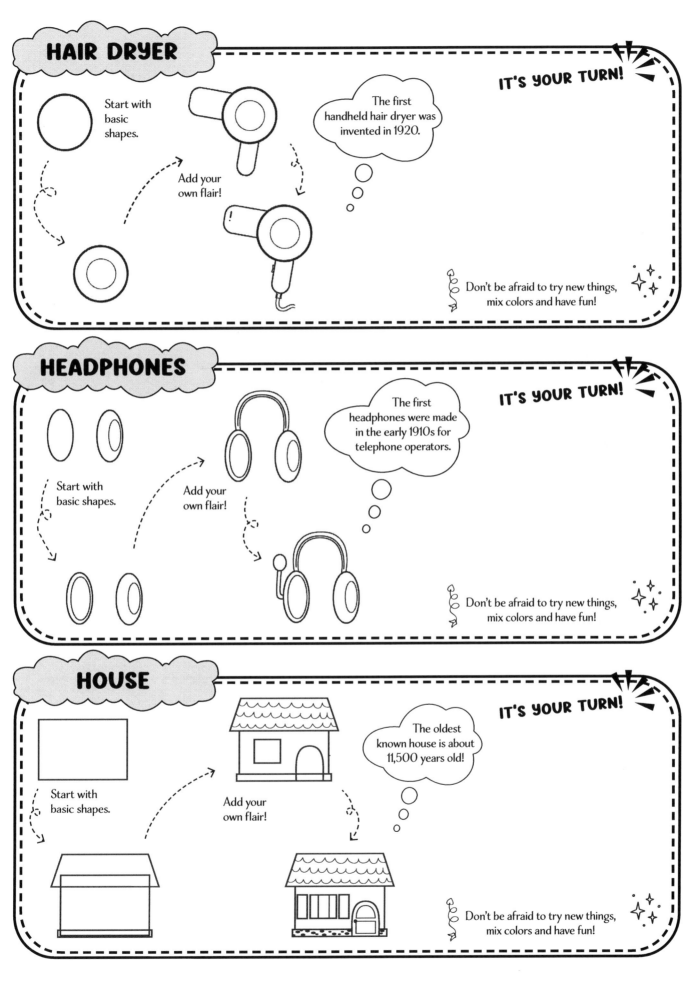

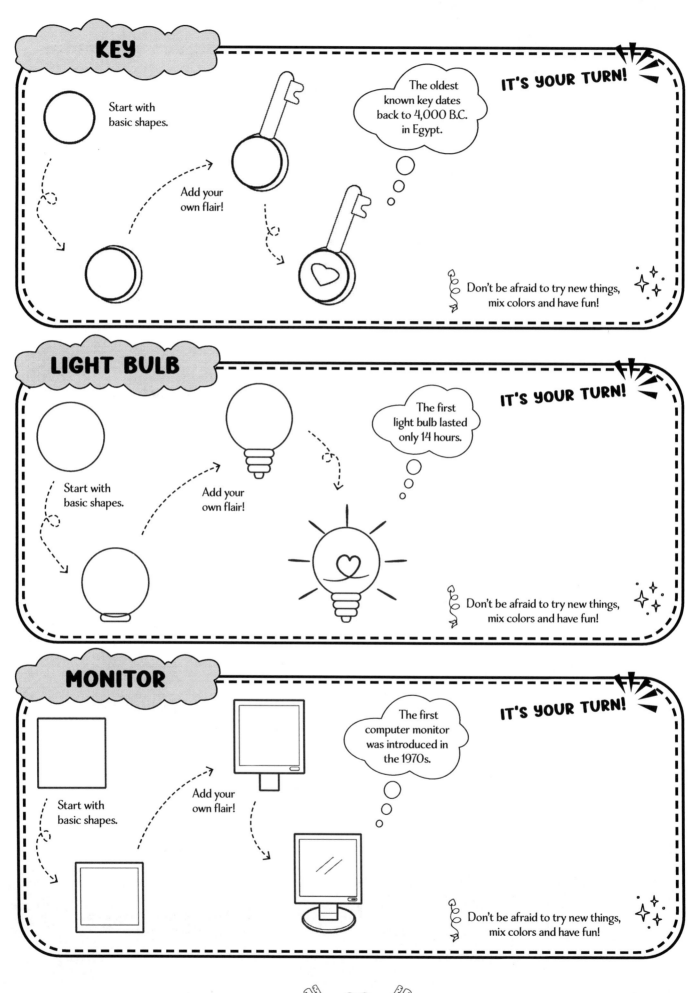

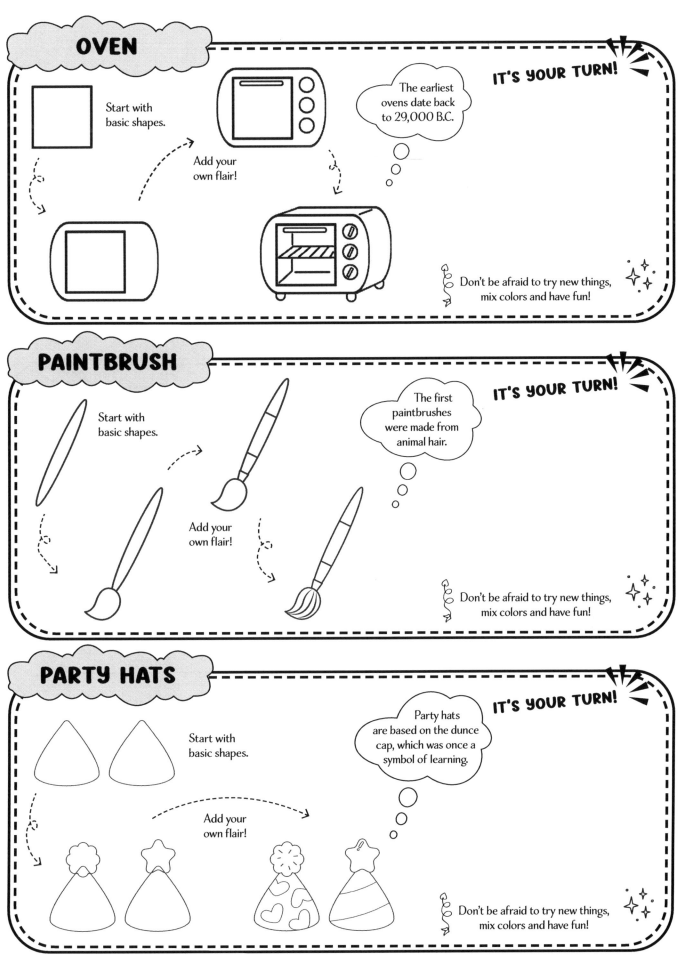

OVEN

Start with basic shapes.

Add your own flair!

IT'S YOUR TURN!

The earliest ovens date back to 29,000 B.C.

Don't be afraid to try new things, mix colors and have fun!

PAINTBRUSH

Start with basic shapes.

Add your own flair!

IT'S YOUR TURN!

The first paintbrushes were made from animal hair.

Don't be afraid to try new things, mix colors and have fun!

PARTY HATS

Start with basic shapes.

Add your own flair!

IT'S YOUR TURN!

Party hats are based on the dunce cap, which was once a symbol of learning.

Don't be afraid to try new things, mix colors and have fun!

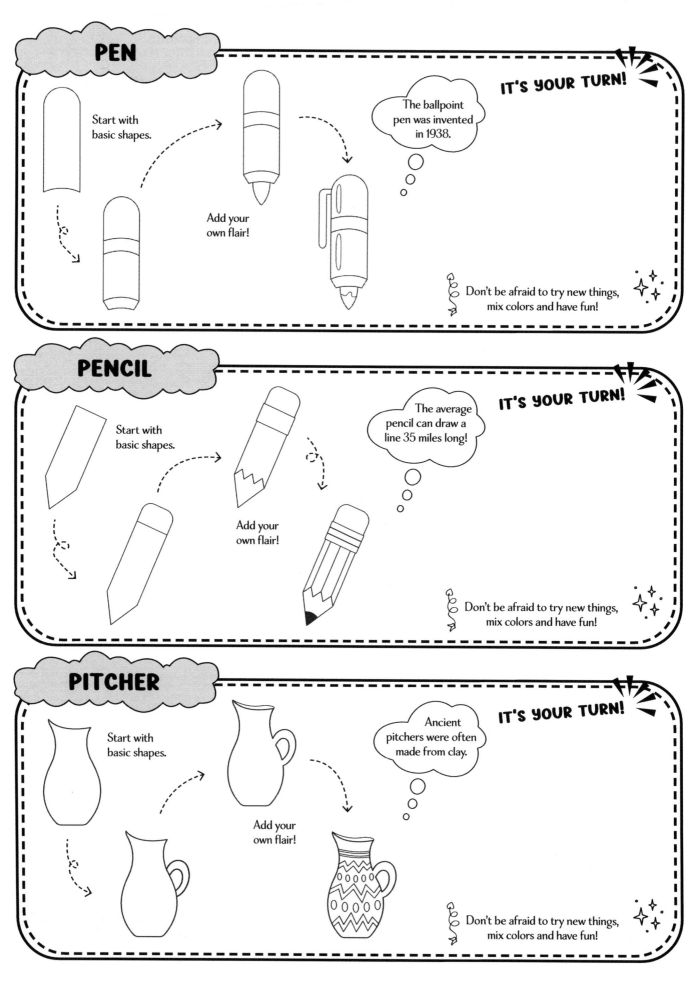

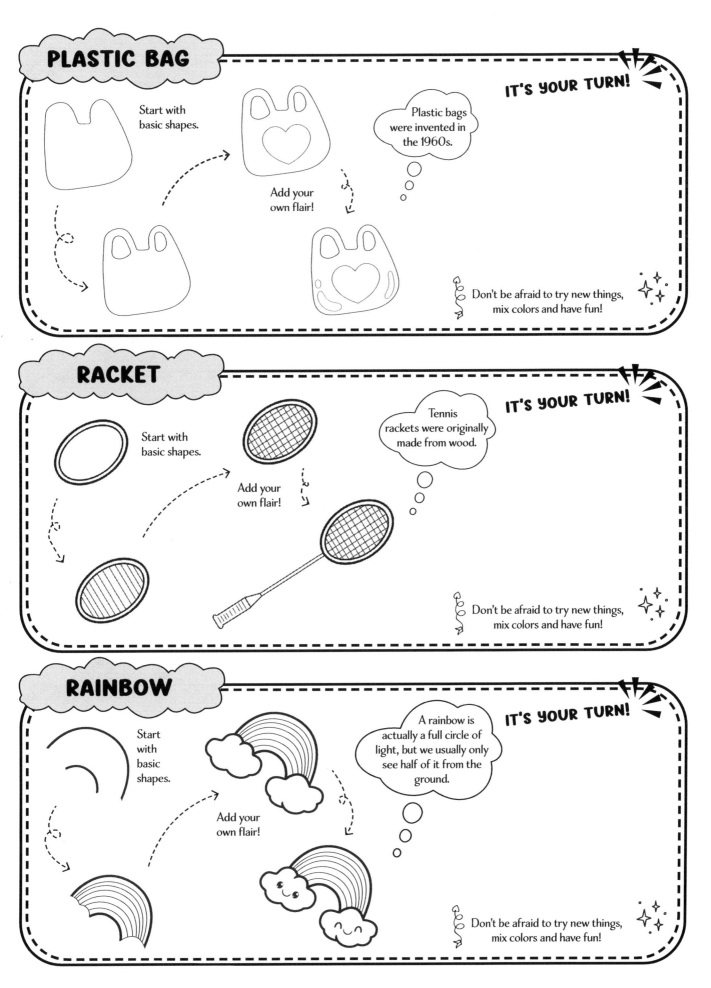

RIBBON

Start with basic shapes.

Add your own flair!

Ribbons were originally used to show social status.

IT'S YOUR TURN!

Don't be afraid to try new things, mix colors and have fun!

SCISSORS

Start with basic shapes.

Add your own flair!

The oldest known scissors date back to ancient Egypt.

IT'S YOUR TURN!

Don't be afraid to try new things, mix colors and have fun!

SHAMPOO

Start with basic shapes.

Add your own flair!

The word "shampoo" comes from a Hindi word meaning "to massage."

IT'S YOUR TURN!

SHAMPOO

Don't be afraid to try new things, mix colors and have fun!

IT'S YOUR TURN!

Start with basic shapes.

Add your own flair!

The first modern sink with running water was invented in 1820.

Don't be afraid to try new things, mix colors and have fun!

STRAW HAT

IT'S YOUR TURN!

Start with basic shapes.

Add your own flair!

Straw hats have been worn since ancient times to protect from the sun.

Don't be afraid to try new things, mix colors and have fun!

SUITCASE

IT'S YOUR TURN!

Start with basic shapes.

Add your own flair!

The first wheeled suitcase was invented in 1970.

Don't be afraid to try new things, mix colors and have fun!

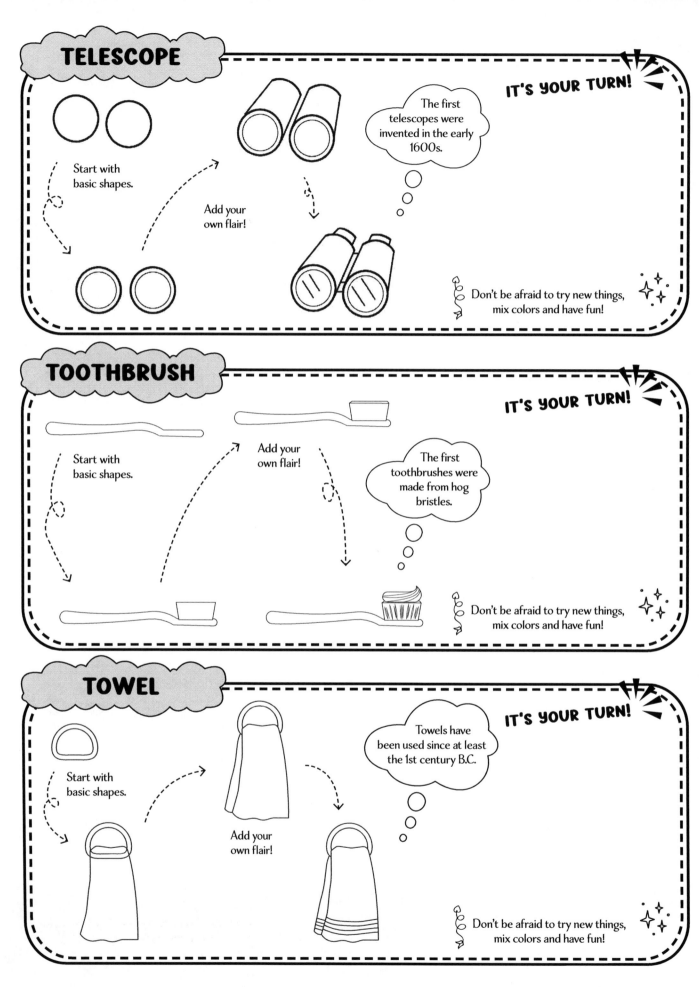

TELESCOPE

IT'S YOUR TURN!

Start with basic shapes.

Add your own flair!

The first telescopes were invented in the early 1600s.

Don't be afraid to try new things, mix colors and have fun!

TOOTHBRUSH

IT'S YOUR TURN!

Start with basic shapes.

Add your own flair!

The first toothbrushes were made from hog bristles.

Don't be afraid to try new things, mix colors and have fun!

TOWEL

IT'S YOUR TURN!

Start with basic shapes.

Add your own flair!

Towels have been used since at least the 1st century B.C.

Don't be afraid to try new things, mix colors and have fun!

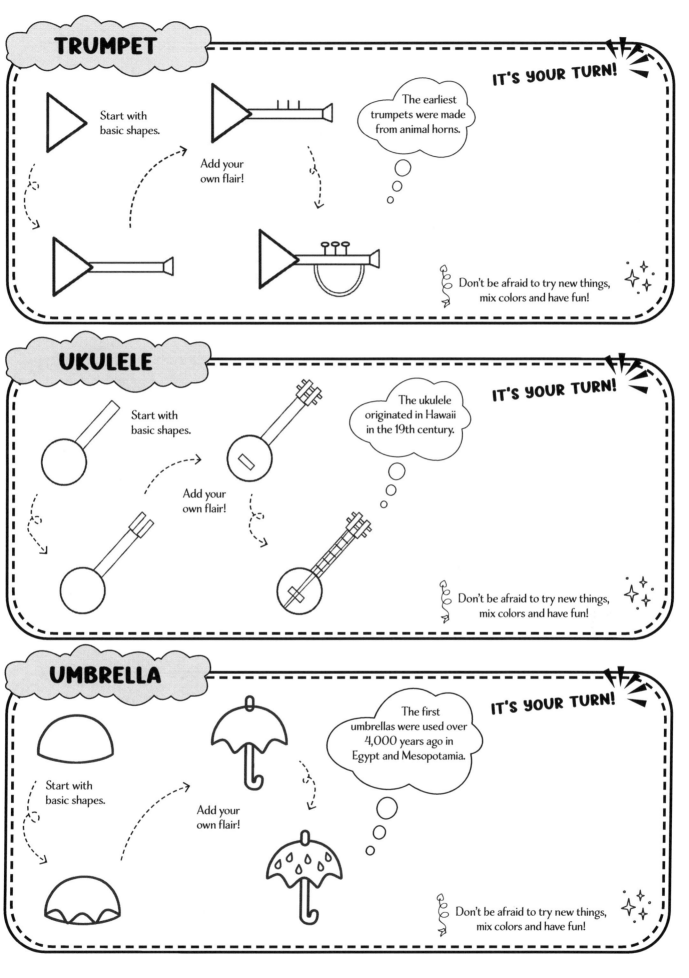

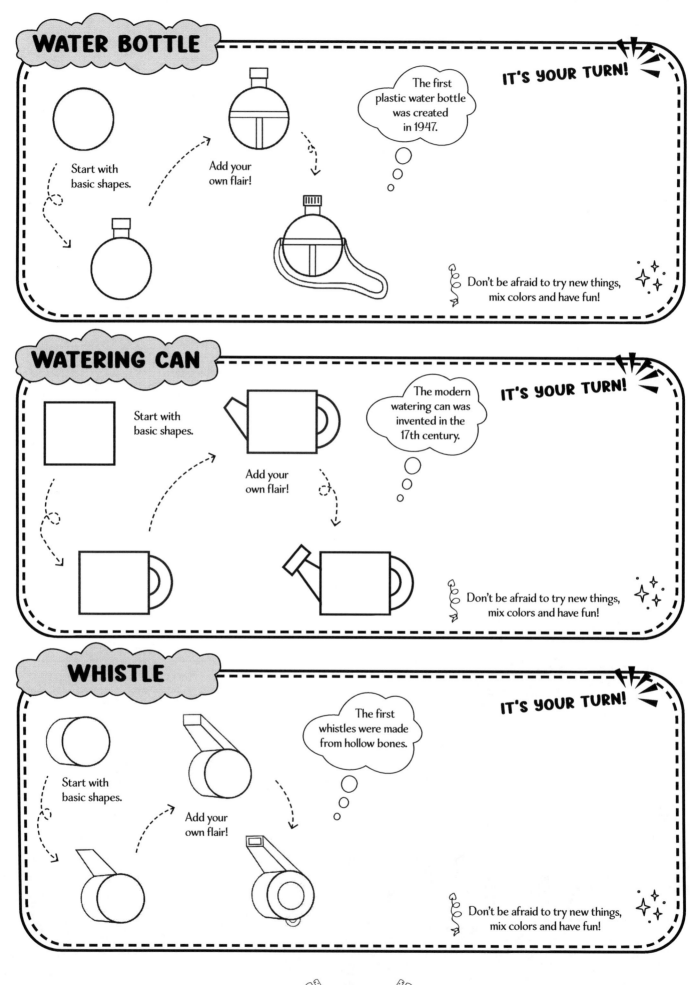

WATER BOTTLE

IT'S YOUR TURN!

Start with basic shapes.

Add your own flair!

The first plastic water bottle was created in 1947.

Don't be afraid to try new things, mix colors and have fun!

WATERING CAN

IT'S YOUR TURN!

Start with basic shapes.

Add your own flair!

The modern watering can was invented in the 17th century.

Don't be afraid to try new things, mix colors and have fun!

WHISTLE

IT'S YOUR TURN!

Start with basic shapes.

Add your own flair!

The first whistles were made from hollow bones.

Don't be afraid to try new things, mix colors and have fun!

YOU ARE AWESOME!

That was a lot of things to draw and you did great! Now you can draw almost everything on your notebooks, greeting cards, and even on posters that you can hang on your wall.

You can even give your drawings as gifts to your friends and family! There are so many things you can do with what you learned to draw.

What do you want to draw next? Keep practicing and master your drawing skills. Check out our other how-to-draw books so you can draw even more things!

Happy drawing!

Made in the USA
Columbia, SC
05 December 2024

48513664R00063